The Official Arsenal Quiz Book

The Official Arsenal Quiz Book

LES GOLD

First published in Great Britain in 2002 by
Hamlyn, a division of Octopus Publishing Group Ltd
2–4 Heron Quays, London E14 4JP

ISBN 0 600 60632 5

A CIP catalogue record for this book is available from the British Library

Printed and bound in the United Kingdom by Mackays of Chatham

C O N T E N T S

QUESTIONS   9

EARLY DAYS   10
FA CUP FINAL – 1950   11
FLOODLIT FOOTBALL   12
AUTHOR! AUTHOR! – PART 1   13
  PART 2   14
KITS, COLOURS AND SPONSORS   15
WHAT'S MY NAME?   16
AFTER THEY WERE GUNNERS – PART 1   17
  PART 2   18
IT'S ALL ABOUT CRICKET, OLD CHAP!   19
THE NAME GAME – PART 1   20
  PART 2   21
TRUE OR FALSE? – PART 1   22
HIGHBURY STADIUM   23
WHO BOUGHT ME? – PART 1   24
  PART 2   25
THE MAGNIFICENT MACS   26
NORTH LONDON DERBIES   27
ENGLISH HEROES   28
SUPER SCOTS   29
WELSH WONDERS   30
IRISH ICONS   31
WHO AM I? – PRE-WAR   33
  1940S/50S   35
  1960S/70S   37
  1980S/90S   39
CLUB RECORDS   41
FA CUP FINAL 1971   42
FA CUP FINAL 1979   43
ARSENAL GREATS – CHARLIE BUCHAN   44
  BOB JOHN   45
  TOM PARKER   46
  DAVID JACK   47
  CLIFF BASTIN   48
  GEORGE MALE   49
  ALEX JAMES   50
  THE COMPTON BROTHERS   51
  TED DRAKE   52
  JIMMY LOGIE   53
  JOE MERCER   54
  JACK KELSEY   55
  GEORGE EASTHAM   56
  GEORGE ARMSTRONG   57
  JOE BAKER   58

FRANK MCLINTOCK 59
JOHN RADFORD 60
PAT RICE 61
CHARLIE GEORGE 62
LIAM BRADY 63
DAVID O'LEARY 64
KENNY SANSOM 65
DAVID ROCASTLE 66
IAN WRIGHT 67
DAVID SEAMAN 68
TONY ADAMS 69
ALAN SMITH 70
LEE DIXON 71
DENNIS BERGKAMP 72
THIERRY HENRY 73
THE MANAGERS – HERBERT CHAPMAN 74
TOM WHITTAKER 75
JACK CRAYSTON 76
GEORGE SWINDIN 77
BILLY WRIGHT 78
BERTIE MEE 79
TERRY NEILL 80
DON HOWE 81
GEORGE GRAHAM 82
BRUCE RIOCH 83
ARSÈNE WENGER 84
MANAGING AFTER THE GUNNERS – PART 1 85
PART 2 86
CHAMPIONSHIP SEASONS – 1930/31 87
1932/33 88
1933/34 89
1934/35 90
1937/38 91
1947/48 92
1970/71 93
1988/89 94
1990/91 95
1997/98 96
FA CUP SEMI-FINALS – PART 1 97
PART 2 98
DEBUTS – PART 1 99
PART 2 100
BEFORE THE GUNNERS – PART 1 101
PART 2 102
PART 3 103

CONTENTS

CAPITAL GUNNERS – PART 1	104
PART 2	105
THE NAME GAME – EXTRA	106
NATIVE COUNTRIES – PART 1	107
PART 2	108
CLUB NICKNAMES	109
MULTIPLE CHOICE – PART 1	110
PART 2	111
GREAT GAMES – V NEWCASTLE	112
V MANCHESTER UNITED	113
V ANDERLECHT	114
V SPURS	115
ARSENAL NOW	116
LEAGUE APPEARANCES	117
OPPOSITION GROUNDS	118
FA YOUTH CUP	119
ARSENAL AT WAR	120
FA CUP APPEARANCES	121
FA CUP OPPONENTS	122
THE FA CHARITY SHIELD	123
THE MISSING LINK	124
TRUE OR FALSE? – PART 2	125
ARSENAL V MANCHESTER UNITED	127
ARSENAL V LIVERPOOL	128
CLUB HISTORY – PART 1	129
PART 2	130
PUBLIC HONOURS	131
THE FA CUP SEMI-FINALS	132
FAMOUS SUPPORTERS	133
GREEN GUNNERS	134
BIRTHPLACES	135
FA CUP FINAL DEFEATS – PART 1	136
PART 2	137
CLUB CAPTAINS	138
ARSENAL IN EUROPE – THE FAIRS CUP	139
THE EUROPEAN FAIRS CUP	140
THE UEFA CUP – PART 1	141
THE EUROPEAN CUP WINNERS' CUP	142
THE EUROPEAN CUP/UEFA	143
CHAMPIONS LEAGUE	
THE UEFA CUP – PART 2	144
OPPOSITION MANAGERS/COACHES	145
GREAT SCOTS	146
ANSWERS	**147**
ACKNOWLEDGEMENTS	192

C
O
N
T
E
N
T
S

QUESTIONS

❓ EARLY DAYS

1 Where did Arsenal's founders congregate to form their new club?

2 In which year?

3 What was the new club called?

4 What was the origin of the new name?

5 Who were the club's first opponents?

6 What was the result of that match?

7 At a meeting in December that year, the founders changed the name of the club to what?

8 To which ground did they move in 1887/88?

9 In their second season (1887/88) they entered a cup competition for the first time. What was it called?

10 In 1889/90 they appeared in the FA Cup for the first time. Who did they play?

11 What was the score?

12 Which three trophies did they win in that season?

13 Increasing gates forced the club to move again. Where did they go?

14 In 1890/91 they moved grounds again. What was the name of their new ground?

15 That season they were beaten in the FA Cup by which team that was recently relegated from the Premiership?

Answers on page 148

❓ FA CUP FINAL – 1950

1 In which month was the final played?

2 What was the score at half-time?

3 Who scored both of Arsenal's goals?

4 Both teams had to change colours. What colour shirts did Arsenal wear?

5 How many times had Arsenal won the FA Cup prior to the 1950 triumph?

6 Which Liverpool player, who was to become a legendary manager, was surprisingly omitted from the Cup final team after appearing in all the previous rounds?

7 What was 'capital' about Arsenal's FA Cup run that season?

8 What honour was given to Arsenal's skipper Joe Mercer on the eve of the final?

9 In which position did Arsenal finish in the League that season?

10 Where were the semi-final and the replay played that season?

11 Which monarch presented the FA Cup to skipper Joe Mercer?

12 Name the manager who guided Arsenal to their FA Cup success.

13 Arsenal's defence remained unchanged throughout their FA Cup campaign except for one occasion. Who was the player who made only a single appearance during that Cup run?

14 Which national sporting hero made his final appearance for Arsenal in that FA Cup final?

15 What mix-up occurred when the medals were presented?

Answers on page 153

FLOODLIT FOOTBALL

❓ FLOODLIT FOOTBALL

1 In the early days of floodlighting, what was the major difference between Arsenal's lighting and that of other clubs?

2 In which year did Arsenal first experiment with matches under floodlights?

3 The first floodlit charity match was played at Highbury in 1951. Which teams took part?

4 Who were Arsenal's opponents in the first major floodlit match at Highbury ?

5 Who scored Arsenal's first competitive goal under floodlights?

6 What was the first floodlit international match played at Highbury?

7 For a majority of years between 1953 and 1962 there was an annual charity match played at the end of each season at Highbury. Who was it between?

8 In which year was the first floodlit League match played at Highbury and who were the opposition?

9 At what time did Saturday winter matches start before floodlighting was introduced?

10 What stipulation did the Football League make before a match could be played under floodlights?

11 Arsenal played Rangers in a prestigious friendly on 8 December 1951. How many people attended the match?

12 Which top Soviet side did Arsenal play in Moscow under lights in 1954/55?

13 In which year did Arsenal first play an FA Cup final under floodlights and who were the opposition?

14 Who was the royal guest when Arsenal played floodlit friendlies against Hibernian in 1952 and a Brazil XI in 1965?

15 What was the last FA Cup semi-final to be played under the Highbury lights?

Answers on page 158

QUESTIONS

❓❓❓❓❓❓❓❓❓❓

AUTHOR! AUTHOR! – PART 1

Which Arsenal players or associates of the club wrote the following books?

1 *Safe Hands*

2 *Rock Bottom*

3 *The Life of Brian*

4 *Ray of Hope*

5 *Captain of Wales*

6 *The Wright Stuff*

7 *Champagne Charlie*

8 *Achieving the Goal*

9 *Revelations of a Football Manager*

10 *Forward Arsenal*

11 *You've Got To Be Crazy*

12 *Football Ambassador*

13 *A Lifetime in Football*

14 *Arsenal from the Heart*

15 *The Arsenal Story*

Answers on page 163

QUESTIONS

AUTHOR! AUTHOR! - PART 2

Which Arsenal players or associates of the club wrote the following books?

1 *Addicted.*

2 *The Glory and the Grief.*

3 *Going Great Guns.*

4 *Win.*

5 *Over the Bar.*

6 *So Far, So Good.*

7 *Football with a Smile.*

8 *A Miller's Tale.*

9 *My Twenty Years of Soccer.*

10 *One Hundred Caps and All That.*

11 *Frankly Speaking.*

12 *The Working Man's Ballet.*

13 *Double Champions.*

14 *Behind the Scenes in Big Football.*

15 *A Little Thing Called Pride*

Answers on page 168

❓ KITS, COLOURS AND SPONSORS

1 When do Arsenal play in their away kit at home?

2 Who were Arsenal's shirt sponsors in 2001/02?

3 What brand name was printed on their shirts?

4 Who were Arsenal's first shirt sponsors?

5 In which season did that sponsorship start?

6 In which season did Arsenal adopt the famous white sleeves?

7 Which manager was the innovator of that famous strip?

8 What Arsenal kit did a journalist describe as 'kitchen curtains'?

9 In which season was it introduced?

10 For which two post-war seasons did Arsenal revert to an all-red shirt?

11 For the FA Cup sixth-round tie with Blackpool in 1953 Arsenal wore an unusual kit for the only time in their history. Describe that strip.

12 Since the war Arsenal have won the FA Cup six times but only three times when they were wearing their famous red and white strip. Name those years.

13 In the 1950s Arsenal used two regular alternative change shirts. What colours were they?

14 From 1933 to 1964 Arsenal's traditional socks were white with hoops. What colour were those hoops?

15 For a short spell in their Woolwich days Arsenal played in an unusual striped kit. What were those colours?

Answers on page 173

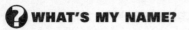

WHAT'S MY NAME?

Which post-war players have the following middle names? Note: the decade in which they signed for Arsenal is in brackets after each name.

1 Jeremiah (2000s)

2 Faxe (1990s)

3 Lauriston (1980s)

4 Cassius (1980s)

5 Carlyle (1980s)

6 Anderson (1970s)

7 Primrose (1960s)

8 Gillen (1960s)

9 John Francombe (1960s)

10 Henderson (1950s)

11 Gillespie (1950s)

12 Cornelius Henry (1950s)

13 Tullis (1940s)

14 Rooney (1940s)

15 Henshall Wilson (1940s)

Answers on page 178

 AFTER THEY WERE GUNNERS – PART 1

Name the clubs the following players joined after leaving Arsenal.

1 Nelson Vivas

2 Chris Kiwomya

3 Andy Cole

4 Perry Groves

5 Niall Quinn

6 Martin Hayes

7 Graham Rix

8 Pat Rice

9 Liam Brady

10 John Radford

11 Frank McLintock

12 John Barnwell

13 Jimmy Logie

14 Ray Bowden

15 Joe Hulme

Answers on page 182

 17

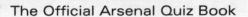

AFTER THEY WERE GUNNERS – PART 2

Name the clubs the following players joined after leaving Arsenal.

1 Eddie McGoldrick

2 John Hartson

3 Andy Linighan

4 Anders Limpar

5 Viv Anderson

6 Steve Gatting

7 Charlie George

8 George Graham

9 Tommy Baldwin

10 Eddie Kelly

11 Jim Furnell

12 Joe Wade

13 Tommy Lawton

14 Ronnie Rooke

15 Bryan Jones

Answers on page 187

❓ IT'S ALL ABOUT CRICKET, OLD CHAP!

1 Which player who made his Arsenal debut in the mid-1970s had a brother who was captain of the England cricket team?

2 Who was the double international who played for Arsenal between 1913 and 1921?

3 Which great cricketer had a benefit match at Highbury in 1949?

4 Which Arsenal keeper once finished top of the bowling averages for Worcestershire County Cricket Club?

5 Which of Chapman's 'greats' shone at both sports?

6 Apart from two famous cricketing brothers who represented Arsenal, name the only other Middlesex cricketer to have had a cricket match at Highbury.

7 Who was the last player to represent England at both football and cricket?

8 Which great post-war Arsenal striker played county cricket for Hampshire?

9 Name the Arsenal player of the 1950s with a bird-like name who also played county cricket for Derbyshire.

10 Who played in over 40 Test matches for England, including a spell as captain, after spending two years at Highbury in the early 1950s?

11 Who once opened the batting for Derbyshire and later became an Arsenal director and club chairman?

12 Which Middlesex wicket keeper was also a central defender for Arsenal?

13 He was a county cricketer for 18 years and an Arsenal player for 9 post-war years during which he played over 300 matches, sadly never in the first team. Name him.

14 Which post-war striker who played in two Arsenal Championship-winning teams also played county cricket for Hampshire?

15 Which legend from Arsenal's early days represented England at both football and cricket? He also played for Aston Villa.

Answers on page 148

? THE NAME GAME – PART 1

These famous people from the world of films or music share their surnames with Arsenal stars. Name both the VIP and player.

1 The producer/star of the film *Annie Hall*.

2 The family of a spoof horror film/TV series.

3 A rock star who starred in *Tommy*.

4 The female star of the thriller *Straw Dogs*.

5 'It's Not Unusual'.

6 The wrinkled actor in the Carry On film series.

7 A star of the satirical war movie *M.A.S.H.*

8 Composer who won an Oscar for his song 'Moon River' in *Breakfast at Tiffany's*.

9 A trumpet-playing legend nicknamed Satchmo.

10 A 1950s actor who co-starred in many films with Doris Day.

11 A veteran Radio Two presenter, recently knighted.

12 An outstanding rock guitarist.

13 Edward G. Robinson once played this 'small' gangster.

14 A blind, black American soul singer.

15 A film star who became a princess.

Answers on page 153

 THE NAME GAME – PART 2

These famous people share their surnames with Arsenal stars. Name both the VIP and the player.

1 The 'Peanut' US president.

2 The black American singer, musician and impersonator, regarded as the world's greatest entertainer.

3 The factory boss in *Coronation Street*.

4 A pipe-smoking Labour leader.

5 The pop superstar whose recording of 'Swing When You're Winning' reached No. 1 at Christmas 2001

6 A regular at Trafalgar Square.

7 The 1960s TV star of *Callan*.

8 A Liberal politician.

9 Cleopatra?

10 The 'Evening, All' policeman.

11 The beautiful star of *Notting Hill*.

12 A US president who was assassinated.

13 The star of the Whitehall farces, famous for dropping his trousers.

14 An American evangelist.

15 This 1960s song described the best mode of transport for getting across the Mersey.

Answers on page 159

THE NAME GAME – PART 2

QUESTIONS

21

TRUE OR FALSE? – PART 1

1 Pat Jennings' first League club was Tottenham Hotspur.

2 David Price played in the FA Cup finals of 1978, 1979 and 1980.

3 Sammy Nelson played more times for Northern Ireland than Pat Rice.

4 For 35 years Arsenal manager George Allison was the London correspondent of the *New York Herald*.

5 Denis Compton once played county cricket for Middlesex at Lord's and League football for Arsenal at Highbury on the same day.

6 Steve Walford replaced David Price in the 1979 FA Cup final.

7 Pat Rice's nickname was 'Crispy'.

8 Arsenal's assistant physio Colin Lewin is brother of the first team's physio Gary.

9 George Graham wore the number 8 shirt in the 1972 FA Cup final.

10 David Seaman played for a First Division side (pre-Premier League) that was knocked out of the FA Cup by a non-League outfit.

11 Gerry Ward is the youngest ever player to represent Arsenal in a major match.

12 Arsène Wenger is the third Arsenal manager whose surname starts with the letter 'W'.

13 Alan Ball commanded Arsenal's first six-figure transfer fee.

14 Sol Campbell was the youngest player to captain England since Bobby Moore.

15 Arsenal striker Ronnie Rooke was over 35 years old when Arsenal purchased him from Fulham in 1946. In the next two seasons he played 66 League games, scored 54 goals and won a League Championship medal.

Answers on page 164

 HIGHBURY STADIUM

1 Which road is in Arsenal's official Highbury address?

2 In which year did Arsenal move to Highbury?

3 What did the 21-year lease cost Arsenal?

4 Who was the architect who designed Highbury?

5 What religious stipulation did Arsenal have to agree to when the stadium was first built?

6 Who were Arsenal's first League opponents at Highbury?

7 What was the original name of the local underground station?

8 What is Arsenal's record attendance at Highbury?

9 In which year was that record set and who were the opposition?

10 During the Second World War what part did the stadium play in the war effort?

11 Which Highbury stand was demolished by enemy action during the Second World War?

12 What are the pitch dimensions at Highbury?

13 In 1999 Arsenal announced proposals to move their stadium to a new site. Where will the new stadium be?

14 In keeping with other major clubs, the proposed new stadium will be an all-seater. What will be its capacity?

15 Why can the West and East Stands at Highbury never be demolished?

Answers on page 169

❓ WHO BOUGHT ME? – PART 1

Name the Arsenal manager who bought the following players.

1 Peter Simpson

2 Andy Ducat

3 Jimmy Brain

4 Ian Ure

5 Steve Williams

6 John Hollins

7 Dennis Bergkamp

8 Matthew Upson

9 Vic Groves

10 Colin Addison

11 Ted Drake

12 Doug Lishman

13 Bob John

14 Tommy Docherty

15 Charlie Buchan

Answers on page 174

WHO BOUGHT ME? – PART 2

Name the Arsenal manager who bought the following players.

1 Laurie Brown

2 Tom Whittaker

3 Tom Parker

4 Don Howe

5 Alex Manninger

6 Alf Baker

7 Alan Skirton

8 Charlie Nicholas

9 Paul Mariner

10 Joe Baker

11 Joe Mercer

12 Brian Kidd

13 John Hartson

14 Ronnie Rooke

15 Don Roper

Answers on page 178

QUESTIONS

THE MAGNIFICENT MACS

THE MAGNIFICENT MACS

1 Who made his debut in front of Arsenal's lowest post-war crowd and transferred to Huddersfield Town a season later?

2 Which full-back was affectionately known as Flint?

3 Which Republic of Ireland international started his League career with Northampton Town and was transferred to Manchester City?

4 Who was signed from Hibernian in the early 1960s and made over a hundred appearances for Arsenal?

5 Who was arguably Arsenal's greatest ever skipper?

6 Which Scottish international played for Great Britain against the Rest of Europe in 1947?

7 Which prolific goalscorer managed Fulham and Huddersfield after his playing career had ended?

8 Name the Irish international keeper who was transferred by Arsenal to Fulham in 1964.

9 Which young defender made his Arsenal League debut away at Sheffield Wednesday in May 1993?

10 Who was the Scottish wing-forward who won a Championship medal with Arsenal in 1947/48?

11 Who played his part in an historic Arsenal side before being transferred to Wolverhampton Wanderers in 1975?

12 Who came to Arsenal as an outside-left but converted to goalkeeper and made 23 League appearances between 1958 and 1964?

13 Which Northern Ireland international made over a hundred appearances for Arsenal before being transferred to Portsmouth in 1928?

14 Which young defender brought over from Dublin made his only League appearance for Arsenal as a substitute in the away match at Newcastle in May 2000?

15 Which midfield player from the 1970s/80s era made 38 League appearances in 1984 and then was transferred to Oxford United?

Answers on page 183

❓ NORTH LONDON DERBIES

1 In which year was the first ever League meeting between Arsenal (then Woolwich) and Tottenham Hotspur?

2 What was the result of that game?

3 Name the Arsenal hero who had joined Spurs in 1905 for the grand transfer fee of £70.

4 Who was the first Arsenal player to score a hat-trick against Spurs?

5 Which wing-forward left Spurs to join Arsenal in 1949 and played in two FA Cup finals during his Highbury days?

6 An Arsenal international midfielder scored only two goals in his 162 games for the club, but they were both in the same match against Spurs. Who was he?

7 Who was the first Arsenal player to be sent off in a North London derby?

8 Before January 2002, how many times since the war has the derby match ended in a 4–4 draw?

9 During a derby match in the late 1970s a Spurs player, who later joined Arsenal, was sent off for foul play. Who was he?

10 Who scored the winning goal when Arsenal defeated Spurs in the 1993 FA Cup semi-final?

11 Which Arsenal player has scored the most goals for Arsenal against Spurs?

12 Prior to 2001/02 how many times have Arsenal met Spurs in the FA Cup?

13 Which Arsenal player has made the most appearances in derby games?

14 In the 1960s he was the only player to play for both clubs in derby matches in the same season. Who was he?

15 Name the first Arsenal player to have a testimonial match against Spurs.

Answers on page 187

QUESTIONS

 27

❓ ENGLISH HEROES

1 Which Arsenal player has made the most appearances for England?

2 Who was Arsenal's first English international?

3 Which post-war player was chosen to represent England after a mere 12 games for Arsenal?

4 An Arsenal player held the record for the most appearances for England between the two world wars. Name him.

5 Who was in the 1966 World Cup squad but never made an appearance throughout the tournament?

6 He was an ex 'tractor boy' who made a single England appearance while at Arsenal. Name him.

7 Which pre-war Arsenal and England midfield star made Norman 'Bite yer legs' Hunter look docile?

8 How many Arsenal players represented England in the infamous 'Battle of Highbury' match in 1934?

9 Who were they?

10 Which Arsenal star was the first player to replace the great Tom Finney?

11 Who was the first Arsenal player born after the 1966 World Cup to be capped by England?

12 In the 1970s only one England player scored a hat-trick and he was an Arsenal striker who was to notch five goals in a single match. Name him.

13 Which two Arsenal players captained England in the 1930s?

14 Against which team did David Seaman make a phenomenal save in a penalty shoot-out in the European Championship of 1996?

15 In the 1970s an Arsenal goalkeeper's sole appearance for England was half a match. Name the goalie.

Answers on page 148

🤔 SUPER SCOTS

1 Name Arsenal's Scottish international who was born in Chesterfield.

2 Who was Arsenal's first Scottish international player?

3 Which Arsenal star started his career with Blackpool and finished it with Hereford United, during which time he represented Scotland?

4 Who holds the record for making the most international appearances for Scotland while an Arsenal player?

5 Which pre-war star represented Scotland on eight occasions, four times with the club he was bought from and four times with Arsenal?

6 Who won a Championship medal and played in two FA Cup finals for Arsenal as well as representing Scotland?

7 Name either player who won a Championship medal and played in two FA Cup finals for Arsenal, as well as representing Scotland?

8 Which Scottish international star, born in Aldershot, played for his country before joining Arsenal in 1974?

9 In the late 1950s Arsenal had three representatives in two consecutive Scottish matches. Who were they?

10 Name the two Arsenal managers who have represented Scotland.

11 Who played over 320 matches for Arsenal during which time he made only one appearance for Scotland?

12 Name the 'big' buy who, though never fulfilling his potential, represented the Scotland Under-23 side on two occasions.

13 Which pre-war Scottish international keeper won a Championship medal with Arsenal?

14 Who was the Scottish Under-21 international who played for Arsenal between 1988 and 1996 and was loaned out to Luton Town and Brighton before leaving Highbury?

15 How many Scottish internationals played in Arsenal's 1947/48 League Championship-winning side?

Answers on page 153

❓❓❓❓❓❓❓❓❓❓

❓ WELSH WONDERS

1 Which big-money star was bought for a record fee from a Midlands club but never quite lived up to his potential?

2 Who was Arsenal's first Welsh international player?

3 Who made his Arsenal debut in the match that saw the end of Joe Mercer's career and was an established Welsh international by the end of the year?

4 This Welsh star was one of George Graham's last purchases and has since played for numerous clubs. Name him.

5 Name the player who was killed in action during the Second World War. His brother, who was to become a Welsh international, was also on the staff.

6 During the 1950s Arsenal had four Welsh stars playing in the same international side. Who were they?

7 Who was the Double-winning Welsh international who was bought from Northampton Town in 1969?

8 Which big-money, versatile star scored 28 goals in 64 appearances during an injury-riddled Arsenal career?

9 Who was Arsenal's only pre-war Welsh international keeper?

10 Which pre-war Welsh star won three Championships and an FA Cup medal while a Gunner?

11 Whose brilliant Arsenal career was sadly finished when he was injured playing for Wales against Brazil?

12 Which great player from the Chapman era was captain of his club as well as Wales?

13 Who was bought and sold by Wrexham and won many international honours but sadly not during his time at Highbury?

14 Which Welsh international captain was bought by Arsenal from Crystal Palace in 1981?

15 Name the Welsh Gunner who masterminded Northampton's supersonic rise through the divisions of the Football League.

Answers on page 159

IRISH ICONS

1 Who was the Irish international central defender signed from a London club in the 1950s who had a short, injury-riddled Arsenal career?

2 Who was the Arsenal defender born in London who apparently complained about the length of the opponents' national anthem on his debut for the Republic, only to be told it was Ireland's own?

3 Which was Irish keeper Pat Jennings' last registered club?

4 Who was the Eire star who played for Arsenal immediately after the war, represented the Republic at both football and rugby, and was also the national sprint and long jump champion?

5 Besides Pat Jennings, name the other Irish international keeper who has played for Arsenal since the war.

6 Who played many times for Northern Ireland and was Arsenal's 'caretaker' manager for a short period?

7 Which Republic defender was an Arsenal player for nine years before being transferred to Norwich City on a free transfer in 1983?

8 Who was the diminutive tricky wing-forward who joined Arsenal in 1954 and gained 15 Republic of Ireland caps during his seven years at Highbury?

9 Which Irish international keeper joined Arsenal in 1948 but won his caps after being transferred to Portsmouth and played in the 1958 World Cup?

10 Which Arsenal and Republic of Ireland player smashed many Highbury records before progressing to Premier League management?

11 Name the Republic star who played at Maine Road after leaving Arsenal in 1990.

IRISH ICONS CONT.

12 Who was the Republic star who scored 108 goals for Arsenal and went on to play for Ajax (Holland), Le Havre (France) and other clubs after leaving Highbury?

13 Which Eire international was transferred from Arsenal to Sheffield United in 1948 and went on to play in Italy for Turin, Udinese and Brescia?

14 Whose nickname was Chippy?

15 Which stalwart Irish defender was once accused by the FA (and found guilty) of 'mooning'?

Answers on page 164

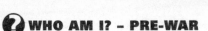 WHO AM I? – PRE-WAR

1 I was quite a boy.

I held an Arsenal record for almost 50 years.

I played for England 21 times.

2 I started my League career with Chesterfield.

I played for both of the North London clubs.

Although I played only 18 League matches, I still won a League Championship medal.

3 I was 35 when I made my debut for Arsenal in 1925.

I captained Arsenal in an FA Cup final.

You used to read me monthly.

4 I was born in Dublin in 1905.

I joined Arsenal from Sheffield United in 1933.

I played 21 League matches in Arsenal's Championship-winning side of 1935 but only one match the following season when they retained the title.

5 I was born in Barnsley in 1909.

I won two League Championship medals and one FA Cup winner's medal with Arsenal in the 1930s.

I returned to the club that I had left to join Arsenal.

6 I was a Welsh international.

I made sure I always washed my jersey.

I played 142 League games for Arsenal.

7 I was born in 1886.

After joining Woolwich Arsenal in 1905 I played in 175 League matches and scored 19 goals.

I won full international honours at both football and cricket.

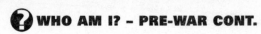

? WHO AM I? – PRE-WAR CONT.

8 I was probably the finest utility player ever to play for Arsenal.

I played only one more match for Arsenal after helping them win the FA Cup in 1930.

My nickname was 'Doughy'.

I was a Cornishman who played for Plymouth Argyle.

9 I won three major honours with Arsenal.

I became a 'Geordie' after gunning.

10 I was 'the' skipper.

I won every possible honour.

I managed Blackburn Rovers after playing.

11 I was involved in the great Chapman era.

I managed Charlton Athletic after the war.

I was called 'The Tiger'.

12 I was called Arsenal's 'greatest'.

I wonder how I never tripped over the hem of my shorts.

I was a member of the 'Blue Wembley Devils'.

13 I was a third back in the Arsenal defensive system.

I missed the 1930 FA Cup final through injury but played in two other finals.

I sadly 'left' during the Second World War.

14 I was an Arsenal record-breaker.

I scored 124 goals for the Gunners.

I was a winner as a manager as well as a player.

15 I played 309 League games, starting with Woolwich.

I spent 16 years with Arsenal.

I took over, sadly, an important Arsenal post.

Answers on page 169

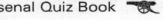

WHO AM I? – 1940s/50s

1 I was a goalkeeper.

I made my League debut in 1946/47.

I was transferred to Portsmouth in the early 1950s.

2 I was transferred to Arsenal for a record fee.

I won Charity Shield winner's medals for the club either side of the Second World War.

A relative of mine was a Double winner.

3 I represented England in the 1952 Olympic Games.

I was signed for Arsenal from an East London club in the mid-1950s.

I lost my defensive place in 1958 to the player I was bought to replace.

4 I joined Arsenal from Walsall.

I scored 125 goals in 226 League matches for the club.

I played in an FA Cup final for Arsenal.

5 I joined Arsenal in 1939.

I played in over 300 games for the club.

I represented my country against 'The Auld Enemy' only once.

6 I won ten amateur caps and one full international cap.

I won a League Championship medal with Arsenal.

I was a journalist for many years with a prominent London newspaper.

7 I was born in Bolton in 1919.

I was transferred from another London club, joining Arsenal in the early 1950s.

I played for my country 23 times.

8 I was an Arsenal player between 1953 and 1962.

I lost my first-team place to Johnny MacLeod.

I finished my League career with 'The Hatters'.

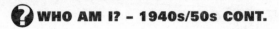

WHO AM I? – 1940s/50s CONT.

9 I was a League Championship and FA Cup winner with Arsenal.

I captained my country.

After retiring I worked as a BBC football adviser.

10 I was transferred from another London team in 1954.

I played 210 League matches, scoring 54 goals.

I went on to manage Leicester City and another London side.

11 I became the Arsenal captain in 1958.

After leaving Arsenal I rejoined the club from which Arsenal had signed me.

I played for and managed my national side.

12 I was signed from a Lancashire side in the late 1950s.

I gained 25 international caps.

Later I became 'the master of clubs'.

13 I joined Arsenal in 1948 from a Sheffield side.

I played in two FA Cup finals.

After my Highbury days were over I played for Leyton Orient and Fulham.

14 I was called 'Peter', although it was not my real name.

I played over 240 games, scoring 53 goals.

I won a Cup winner's medal as a forward but finished my Arsenal career in midfield.

15 I had played League matches for Spurs.

I was signed from an East London side in 1955.

A relation of mine later played for Arsenal.

Answers on page 174

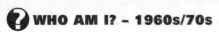
❓ WHO AM I? – 1960s/70s

1 I was a Youth Cup winner with Arsenal.

I went in goal in a semi-final.

I went to Upton and Ewood.

2 I won a League Cup medal, sadly as a loser.

I left the year before the Double.

In 2000 I was assisting Arsenal youth.

3 My brother was a football icon.

I cost a large fee when I came from the valleys.

In 1962 I returned to Wales.

4 I played many times for the men in green.

After Highbury I became a Hornet.

I've assisted Arsène.

5 I'm a Scottish international born in England.

I played for my country before I played for Arsenal.

I finished up as a Villan.

6 I won a Second Division medal with a northern side.

I played between the sticks on 167 occasions.

I finished my career at Drake's Argyle.

7 Strolling, just strolling.

I was a Red Devil after Highbury.

Two Premier League clubs employed me.

8 I was born in Bristol and spent six years at Highbury.

I scored a League Cup hat-trick for Arsenal.

I went across London to the 'Lane'.

9 I was a League Championships and FA Cup-winning Scot.

Sadly, I never represented my country.

I became a Ranger after gunning.

WHO AM I? – 1960s/70s CONT.

10 I was an Irish international star.

I played 253 League matches for Arsenal.

I went to the Den.

11 I captained my club and my country.

After playing over 250 games I went to Boothferry Park.

I managed two London sides.

12 I joined Arsenal from a Black Country outfit.

I gained a single international cap.

I scored an unforgettable goal at Wembley.

13 Blue was my colour.

I played in the Potteries.

Arsenal bought me in 1976.

14 I made the first of my 138 League appearances in 1957.

After Highbury I went to 'Robin Hood' county.

I managed Peterborough, Wolves, Walsall and Northampton Town.

15 I was a back-to-back Wembley winner.

I joined Arsenal from Suffolk.

I now manage a team promoted from the Conference.

Answers on page 178

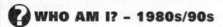

❓ WHO AM I? – 1980s/90s

1 I was born in Scandinavia.

I played only 34 League games before I moved to Italy.

I am now playing once again in the Premier League.

2 I was born in Gap, France, in 1970.

I joined Arsenal from AS Monaco in 1997.

I won League Championship and FA Cup winner's medals for Arsenal in 1998.

3 I made my Arsenal debut in 1985.

I was once on loan to Brighton and Hove Albion.

I played for two other clubs that are still in the Premier League.

4 I joined Arsenal in the mid-1990s.

I played for my European country only once.

I spent a period on loan to Benfica of Portugal.

5 I was a member of Arsenal's Youth Cup-winning side of 1987/88.

I was once dropped.

I was transferred to a West London side in 1997.

6 I turned professional for Arsenal in 1987.

I played for the club at the Riverside Stadium.

I am still playing for a club in the Nationwide First Division.

7 Before I joined Arsenal I was on Birmingham City's, and Oxford United's books.

I have won seven major honours with Arsenal.

I left Arsenal in 2000.

8 I was signed by Arsenal as a goalkeeper.

I never made a single League appearance for the club.

I am now an integral member of the backroom staff.

WHO AM I? – 1980s/90s CONT.

9 I was born in Chesterfield in 1960.

I rejoined the club from which Arsenal had signed me.

I have won two League Championship medals.

10 I was born overseas in 1977.

My four goals were scored in cup competitions at the end of my Arsenal career.

Since leaving Highbury I have played for two Premier League clubs.

11 I was born in Manchester in 1964.

I have represented my country on 22 occasions.

By the end of 2000/2001 I had scored 25 League goals.

12 I was signed from a French side in 1997.

I scored the decisive second goal in a final for Arsenal.

I was transferred to a top Spanish side.

13 I was loaned to the team from which Arsenal had bought me.

I won international honours at both amateur and professional level.

I retired in 1995 after winning two Championship medals with Arsenal.

14 I experienced many personal traumatic times at Highbury.

I was loaned to Brentford in the late 1980s.

I have played for two Premier League sides since leaving Highbury.

15 Although I was born in London, I never represented England.

I broke many club records with Arsenal.

I am now managing a top Premier League side.

Answers on page 183

CLUB RECORDS

Give the Arsenal records for the following categories. Note: up to the end of season 2000/01.

1 Highest win.

2 Heaviest defeat.

3 Biggest Cup victory.

4 Most points scored in a season (two points for a win).

5 Most points scored in a season (three points for a win).

6 Most League goals scored in a season.

7 Highest League scorer in a season.

8 Scorer of the most League goals in aggregate.

9 Scorer of the most League goals in one single match.

10 Player with the most League appearances.

11 Most capped player.

12 Youngest ever player.

13 Player who commanded the highest transfer fee.

14 Record attendance.

15 Record attendance at Wembley.

Answers on page 188

❓ CUP FINAL 1971 – ARSENAL V LIVERPOOL

1 What success did Arsenal achieve by winning this final?

2 What was the score at half-time?

3 Who was Liverpool's legendary manager?

4 Name the two skippers.

5 As there was a clash of colours Arsenal changed to blue shirts. True or false?

6 Who opened the scoring for Liverpool?

7 Eddie Kelly was credited with scoring Arsenal's first goal, but some people thought another player got the final touch. Who was that?

8 What record did Eddie Kelly achieve when he scored Arsenal's equalizing goal?

9 Who was Arsenal's coach that day?

10 Who made the pass that led to Charlie George's winning strike?

11 Who was the Liverpool and England keeper who failed to stop both Arsenal goals?

12 What was the name of the Cup final referee?

13 Which Arsenal star joined Liverpool three years later?

14 Apart from Kelly, who was Arsenal's other substitute that day?

15 How many goals did Charlie George score during that 1971 Cup campaign?

Answers on page 149

❓ CUP FINAL 1979 – ARSENAL V MANCHESTER UNITED

1 What was the score at half-time?

2 Who scored Arsenal's last-gasp Cup-winning goal?

3 What was unique about Brian Talbot's Cup final appearance for Arsenal?

4 As there was a clash of colours, both teams changed. True or false?

5 How many games did it take before Arsenal defeated Sheffield Wednesday in round three?

6 Who was Arsenal's Cup final manager?

7 Who was the manager of Manchester United?

8 Who set up all three of Arsenal's goals?

9 Which Arsenal star joined Manchester United two years later?

10 Name the two team captains.

11 Who had played in six Cup matches in the earlier rounds but missed out on the final?

12 Including this match, how many FA Cup final appearances had Pat Rice made for Arsenal?

13 How much time elapsed between Manchester United's equalizer and Arsenal's winning goal?

14 Who was Arsenal's substitute that day?

15 How many Irishmen were in Arsenal's Cup final side?

Answers on page 154

FA CUP FINAL 1979 – ARSENAL V MANCHESTER UNITED

QUESTIONS

ARSENAL GREATS – CHARLIE BUCHAN

1 Where was Charlie Buchan born?

2 He played as an amateur with which two clubs?

3 With which club did he turn professional?

4 One year and 17 goals later Charlie Buchan joined which big northern club?

5 What scoring record does Charlie still hold for that club?

6 In which year did he become an Arsenal player?

7 How old was he when he moved to Arsenal?

8 What was the unusual transfer deal agreed between the two clubs?

9 How much did Arsenal pay Sunderland at the end of Charlie's first season at Highbury?

10 Charlie gained a First Division Championship medal at Arsenal. True or false?

11 Charlie captained Arsenal in the 1927 Cup final. Arsenal lost, but what was unusual about the winning team?

12 He played 120 matches for Arsenal. How many goals did he score in League and Cup?

13 What was the title of Charlie's autobiography published in 1955?

14 On retiring from playing, Charlie Buchan wrote regular articles for which national newspaper?

15 What was the title of the magazine he founded and edited?

Answers on page 159

 ARSENAL GREATS – BOB JOHN

1 What was Bob John's full name?

2 What nationality was he?

3 In which year did he sign for Arsenal?

4 Which Arsenal manager signed Bob?

5 From which club did Arsenal recruit him?

6 While in the Arsenal reserve side Bob received what honour?

7 Who was club captain when Bob joined Arsenal?

8 How many honours did Bob win with Arsenal?

9 He showed his versatility by playing in which three positions for the Gunners?

10 How many international caps did he win?

11 How many years after his first international appearance did Bob make his last Wales appearance?

12 How many years did he play for Arsenal?

13 In what position does he come in the list of players with the most ever appearances for Arsenal? (As at season 2001/02.)

14 In what year did he bow out of Highbury?

15 Bob then took up a coaching position with which London side?

Answers on page 164

ARSENAL GREATS – BOB JOHN

QUESTIONS

ARSENAL GREATS – TOM PARKER

1 From which club did Arsenal sign Tom Parker?

2 In which year did Tom join Arsenal?

3 What was the 'huge' transfer fee?

4 Which Arsenal manager signed Tom?

5 What honour did that Arsenal manager bestow on Tom?

6 After establishing himself in the Arsenal team, Tom went on a run of how many consecutive matches: (a) 85 (b) 120 (c) 155?

7 While an Arsenal player he won three England caps. True or false?

8 During his Highbury spell he scored 17 goals. How did he score most of them?

9 What was the first FA Cup final that he played in for Arsenal?

10 What was significant about that final?

11 What silverware did Tom Parker win during his Highbury career?

12 How many times was he a runner-up in an FA Cup final?

13 How many years did Tom play for Arsenal?

14 On leaving Arsenal he became manager of which club?

15 In which year did Tom die?

Answers on page 169

ARSENAL GREATS – DAVID JACK

1 What FA Cup final individual record does David Jack hold?

2 What FA Cup club record does he hold?

3 What personal transfer record does he hold?

4 David played for his home town club. Where was it?

5 In which year did he join Arsenal?

6 Which player was he bought to replace?

7 David appeared in how many FA Cup finals?

8 How many League Championship medals did he win?

9 How many times did he play for England?

10 He was the first Arsenal player to captain England. True or false?

11 In which year did David retire from playing?

12 On leaving Highbury he became manager of which club?

13 David's middle names were Bone Nightingale. True or false?

14 How many goals did he score in his 181 League appearances for Arsenal?

15 Why did David always have a room of his own on away trips?

Answers on page 174

❓ ARSENAL GREATS – CLIFF BASTIN

1 What was Cliff Bastin affectionately known as?

2 Cliff won every honour in football before he was 19 years of age. True or false?

3 From which West Country club was he transferred to Arsenal?

4 What was the 'huge' fee?

5 In which year did he join Arsenal?

6 In which position did he begin his Highbury career?

7 What record did he set when he appeared in the 1930 FA Cup final?

8 What disability did he have?

9 What important 'on the field' responsibility was given to Cliff when he was only 18 years of age?

10 What scoring record does he still hold?

11 How many England caps did he win?

12 How many goals did he score for England?

13 Why did Cliff not serve in the armed forces during the Second World War?

14 In which year did Cliff's Arsenal career end?

15 Over half a century later what individual club record does Cliff still hold?

Answers on page 179

❓ ARSENAL GREATS – GEORGE MALE

1 What was George Male's profession before he became a footballer?

2 What was memorable about his debut match for Arsenal?

3 In which year was that League debut?

4 Which Arsenal 'great' did George replace?

5 Before he made his name as a great full-back, what position did George play for Arsenal?

6 How many England caps did he win?

7 Did he ever captain his country?

8 How many winner's medals did he collect at Arsenal?

9 Was he ever on an FA Cup final losing side for Arsenal?

10 In which year did he play his final match for the club?

11 Why was his final match as memorable as his first one?

12 How many goals did he score for Arsenal?

13 How many years did George Male play for Arsenal?

14 What was George's connection with Arsenal after his playing days were over?

15 How old was George when he died?

Answers on page 183

❓ ARSENAL GREATS – ALEX JAMES

1 As a teenager Alex James played for a small Scottish village side called Orbiston Village. He was idolized by a ten-year-old from that village who was to become an Old Trafford legend. Name him.

2 With which Scottish club did 'Wee' Alex start his professional career?

3 From which club did Arsenal buy Alex James?

4 In which year did Alex join Arsenal?

5 Alex was asked to play a new role at Arsenal. What was the difference between his new role and the one he had played at his previous club?

6 Who was the Arsenal manager who signed him?

7 What was different about the way he wore part of his kit?

8 What was his first major honour as an Arsenal player?

9 Alex was to go on strike in 1931 after being refused a pay rise. By way of compensation Arsenal arranged a two-year contract worth £250.00 per annum with a major London department store. What was that store?

10 During his Arsenal career Alex was involved in how many League Championship sides?

11 In which year did he make his final League appearance for Arsenal?

12 Alex later returned to Highbury in what capacity?

13 How many times did Alex represent Scotland while an Arsenal player?

14 In which famous international match was Alex a key player?

15 What is the title of an excellent biography of 'Wee' Alex, published in 1988, and who wrote it?

Answers on page 188

ARSENAL GREATS –
THE COMPTON BROTHERS

1 Which brother is the elder – Denis or Leslie?

2 In which positions did they play?

3 Which brother signed first for Arsenal?

4 Which Arsenal manager signed both of them?

5 For which county cricket side did they both play?

6 Which brother scored more FA Cup goals for Arsenal?

7 Leslie Compton set a goalscoring record in a wartime match against Clapton Orient. What was it?

8 The brothers won the same number of honours during their Arsenal days. What were they?

9 What was significant about the number '38' in Leslie Compton's career?

10 What international record does Leslie still hold?

11 Leslie's final appearance for England was notable for what reasons?

12 When was Denis's final match for Arsenal?

13 How many years did Leslie play for Arsenal?

14 What civic honour was awarded to Denis in 1958?

15 Both players had testimonial matches at Highbury. True or false?

Answers on page 149

? **ARSENAL GREATS – TED DRAKE**

1 Ted Drake scored a hat-trick in his first professional League game. True or false?

2 Ted was born in which county?

3 Which club did he leave to join Arsenal?

4 In which year did he become an Arsenal player?

5 Which Arsenal manager signed Ted?

6 What was the fee?

7 Ted made ten appearances in the remaining League matches of that season. How many goals did he score?

8 The following season he broke the club record for the most League goals scored in a season. How many did he score?

9 During that record-breaking season how many times did Ted score three goals or more in a game: (a) four times (b) five times (c) seven times?

10 In 1935 he smashed the record for the most goals scored in a First Division match. How many goals did he score and on which ground?

11 How many England caps did Ted win?

12 In his 168 League matches for Arsenal, Ted scored 106 goals. True or false?

13 During the Second World War what rank did he hold and in which of the armed forces?

14 He finished his football days with Chelsea. What record did Ted set with them in 1954/55?

15 Drake was made a director and life president of which club?

Answers on page 154

 ARSENAL GREATS – JIMMY LOGIE

1 In which famous city was Jimmy Logie born?

2 In which year did he join Arsenal?

3 The transfer fee was £75. True or false?

4 In which branch of the armed forces did Jimmy serve during the Second World War?

5 In which season did Jimmy make his League debut?

6 That match was a disaster for Arsenal. What was the result?

7 In his first season Jimmy played in which two positions before making the inside-right (number 8) Arsenal jersey his own?

8 For how many seasons was Jimmy a regular in the Arsenal team?

9 How many honours did Jimmy Logie win with Arsenal?

10 What were they?

11 For all the years that he was at Highbury, Jimmy never once dropped below 32 matches per season. True or false?

12 What was the importance of the third goal that he scored against Burnley in 1953?

13 In one of his final matches for Arsenal Jimmy disputed a decision in a friendly match that indirectly led to his departure from Highbury. Who were Arsenal's opponents?

14 Which non-League club did Jimmy join on leaving Highbury?

15 When his playing days were over, what was Jimmy's job at Piccadilly Circus?

Answers on page 160

ARSENAL GREATS – JOE MERCER

1 Where was Joe Mercer born?

2 For which club did Joe play before joining Arsenal?

3 In which year did he join Arsenal?

4 How old was Joe when he joined Arsenal?

5 What was the difference between the role he played at Everton and the new role he adopted at Arsenal?

6 Which Arsenal manager bought Joe?

7 Joe won international honours while at Highbury. True or false?

8 Joe skippered Arsenal to how many major domestic honours?

9 What award was given to Joe in 1950?

10 Joe's Arsenal career ended with a serious injury. With which of his team-mates did he collide?

11 Which club did Joe join on leaving Highbury?

12 What civil honour did he receive in 1976?

13 Joe achieved great managerial success with a flamboyant character as his assistant. Name him.

14 Joe managed England. True or false?

15 In which year did Joe Mercer die?

Answers on page 165

❓ ARSENAL GREATS – JACK KELSEY

1 What was Jack's real first name?

2 From which Welsh club did Arsenal sign Jack?

3 What was Jack's job before he became a professional footballer?

4 When did he make his Arsenal League debut?

5 What was unusual about the result of that match?

6 Who did Jack succeed as Arsenal's keeper?

7 Jack holds the record for the most appearances of any Arsenal goalkeeper. True or false?

8 Arsenal was Jack's only League club. True or false?

9 Apart from his appearances for Wales, which two other representative appearances did he make?

10 Jack once played in two important matches on the same day. Name them.

11 Jack made more appearances for Wales than any other Arsenal Welsh international. True or false?

12 How many major honours did he win with Arsenal?

13 When did Jack retire?

14 Jack was granted a testimonial by Arsenal in May 1963. Who provided the opposition?

15 What was Jack's occupation before he left Arsenal?

Answers on page 170

ARSENAL GREATS – GEORGE EASTHAM

1 With which team did George Eastham start his football career?

2 George Eastham went on strike and won a celebrated High Court case. What was his dispute and what was the outcome?

3 Who was the well-known Chairman of the Professional Footballers Association who handled George's dispute?

4 What was the record fee that Arsenal paid for George?

5 Which Arsenal manager bought George?

6 Because of the contractual dispute, George was not allowed to play in the first team. Who were the opponents when he first played in an Arsenal shirt and what was the competition?

7 The crowd for that match was 10,000. True or false?

8 Which foot did George favour – left or right?

9 Which two Arsenal strikers benefited from George's probing?

10 George and his father, who was a professional with Bolton Wanderers, set an international record. What was it?

11 George's nickname was 'Korkey'. True or false?

12 How many times did George play for England?

13 Who was England's manager when George made his international debut in 1963?

14 Which club did George join on leaving Arsenal?

15 He scored a winning goal for his new club in a Wembley final. What was the match and in which year was it played?

Answers on page 175

❓ ARSENAL GREATS – GEORGE ARMSTRONG

1 Where was George Armstrong born?

2 What was George's nickname?

3 What was his job before he became a professional footballer?

4 In which year did he join Arsenal?

5 Which manager signed George for Arsenal?

6 How tall was George?

7 George made only two full appearances for England. True or false?

8 In what position does he come in the list of players with the most ever appearances for Arsenal?

9 How many goals did he score for Arsenal: (a) more than 50 (b) more than 75 or (c) more than 100?

10 Which three major honours did George win with Arsenal?

11 How many seasons did he play at Arsenal?

12 Who were Arsenal's opponents in George's testimonial match in 1974?

13 To which club was George transferred?

14 In which year?

15 What post did George hold at the time of his death?

Answers on page 179

ARSENAL GREATS – JOE BAKER

1 Where was Joe Baker born?

2 For which London club did he have extensive trials?

3 Which was his first major club?

4 To which club was he transferred in May 1961?

5 Which Scottish superstar played with Joe at his new club?

6 What accident almost cost Joe more than just his football career?

7 In which year did he join Arsenal?

8 What was the fee?

9 Which Arsenal boss signed Joe?

10 Who was Joe's striking partner at Arsenal?

11 How many goals did he score in his 157 appearances for Arsenal?

12 Joe finished his career as manager of which Scottish club?

13 How many England caps did Joe win while he was an Arsenal player?

14 What record did Joe set when he was chosen to play for England?

15 How close did he come to playing in the 1966 World Cup?

Answers on page 184

❓ ARSENAL GREATS – FRANK MCLINTOCK

1 In which district of Glasgow was Frank McLintock born?

2 From which club did Arsenal sign Frank?

3 In which year did Frank become a Gunner?

4 Which Arsenal manager signed Frank?

5 What was the record fee?

6 What position did Frank play when he first joined Arsenal?

7 For a central defender Frank was not excessively tall. What was his height?

8 What was the first major success that Frank had as Arsenal skipper?

9 How many times did he play for Scotland?

10 How many times did he represent his country as an Arsenal player?

11 Which club did Frank join on leaving Highbury?

12 Which defender did Arsenal buy to replace Frank?

13 After his playing career was over, Frank managed which two League clubs?

14 Which civil award did Frank receive in 1972?

15 On which Saturday afternoon television programme is he now a regular panellist?

Answers on page 188

ARSENAL GREATS – JOHN RADFORD

1 In which county was John Radford born?

2 John played in a successful Arsenal FA Youth Cup-winning side. True or false?

3 In which year did he make his League debut?

4 John never scored more than 20 goals in total in a season. True or false?

5 What was the first major final he played in for Arsenal?

6 How many League matches did John play in the Double year?

7 What club honour did he win in 1967/68 and 1972/73?

8 In which year did John make his England debut?

9 Which manager selected John to play for England?

10 How many international appearances did John make?

11 How many Arsenal managers did John play under?

12 John was granted a testimonial match at Highbury in 1977. Who provided the opposition?

13 For which two League clubs did John play after leaving Highbury?

14 In which seasons?

15 Which non-League side did John help to win the trophy final in 1981 before becoming their general manager?

Answers on page 149

 ARSENAL GREATS – PAT RICE

1 In which year and in which city was Pat Rice born?

2 In which year did he sign professional forms for Arsenal?

3 Who were Arsenal's opponents in Pat's first game?

4 And in which season?

5 In his early days at Arsenal Pat played in the team that won the FA Youth Cup. What season was that and who did they beat in the final?

6 Whose positional move to midfield allowed Pat to gain a regular first-team spot at full-back in August 1970?

7 What honours did Pat help the club to achieve at the end of that season?

8 In seasons 1971/72, 1975/76, 1976/77 what rare feat did Pat achieve?

9 How many times did Pat represent Northern Ireland?

10 In which year was he appointed club captain?

11 In how many FA Cup finals did Pat play for Arsenal?

12 In which year did Pat leave Highbury and who did he join?

13 What was Pat's rare Double achievement?

14 Pat was manager of Arsenal. True or false?

15 Which wing-forward superstar did Pat rave about as his all-time favourite player?

Answers on page 154

QUESTIONS

The Official Arsenal Quiz Book

ARSENAL GREATS – CHARLIE GEORGE

1 Which of Charlie George's goals helped create Arsenal history?

2 How many League goals did Charlie score in his first season at Arsenal?

3 Which major trophy did he play a prominent part in Arsenal winning that first season?

4 Who were the opposition in Charlie's first FA Cup tie?

5 Why did Charlie miss the first five months of his second season at Arsenal?

6 What number shirt did he wear in the 1971 FA Cup final?

7 How many FA Cup finals did he play in for Arsenal?

8 What was Charlie affectionately known as at Highbury?

9 In which year did he leave Arsenal?

10 Which team seemed certain to sign Charlie when Arsenal made him available for transfer?

11 Which club did he eventually join after leaving Arsenal?

12 How old was Charlie when he left Highbury?

13 Charlie played for England while an Arsenal player. True or false?

14 Who was the England manager who gave Charlie his place in the England side?

15 Charlie played for which two south-coast teams?

Answers on page 160

ARSENAL GREATS – CHARLIE GEORGE

QUESTIONS

62

❓ ARSENAL GREATS – LIAM BRADY

1 Where was Liam Brady born?

2 What was Liam's 'real' first name?

3 When did he first join Arsenal?

4 Liam was signed by Arsenal manager Terry Neill. True or false?

5 For which English clubs did his brothers Pat and Ray play?

6 In which year did Liam make his Arsenal debut?

7 How old was he when he played his first senior game?

8 He was only a substitute in that first match. Who did he replace?

9 In Liam's early Highbury days which manager enquired about his nationality?

10 What was the first major honour Liam won during his Highbury days?

11 What club honour did he win a record three times?

12 Name the four Italian clubs Liam joined after leaving Arsenal.

13 On returning to England, which League club did he join?

14 After retiring from playing in 1990, Liam tried his hand at managing which two clubs?

15 Liam was nicknamed 'Chippy' because he loved eating chips. True or false?

Answers on page 165

? ARSENAL GREATS – DAVID O'LEARY

1 Republic of Ireland pivot David O'Leary was born in North London. True or false?

2 With which great northern side did he have trials?

3 Which Arsenal manager signed David?

4 What was the first major trophy David won with Arsenal?

5 David's younger brother played for Celtic and was also an Irish international. What is his name?

6 Why is the number '1,000' significant in David's soccer records?

7 For how many years was Highbury David's 'second home' as a professional?

8 Only one other Arsenal star had spent longer at Highbury than David. Name him.

9 How many appearances did David make for Arsenal?

10 How many goals did he score?

11 How many times did he play for the Republic of Ireland?

12 How many international goals did he score?

13 Who were the opposition for David's farewell match?

14 David left Arsenal in style! What significant match was his finale?

15 Which club did he join?

Answers on page 170

ARSENAL GREATS – KENNY SANSOM

1 What Arsenal record does Kenny Sansom hold?

2 Which club did Kenny have trials with?

3 Which club did he have success with prior to joining Arsenal?

4 Which prolific duo coached him at that club?

5 What award did he win in 1979/80 and for the next eight years?

6 In which year did Kenny join Arsenal?

7 The fee was a record for a full-back. True or false?

8 As part of the deal, two Arsenal players moved to Crystal Palace. Who were they?

9 What was unusual about Clive Allen's transfer?

10 Which Arsenal manager negotiated the transfer?

11 Which Arsenal full-back was Kenny bought to replace?

12 Kenny had played for England before he joined Arsenal. True or false?

13 In which season did he become Arsenal club captain?

14 During his eight-year stint at Highbury, Kenny won only one major trophy with Arsenal. What was it and in which year did he win it?

15 When Kenny left Arsenal in 1988 which northern club did he join?

Answers on page 175

ARSENAL GREATS – DAVID ROCASTLE

1 What was David Rocastle's nickname?

2 In which year did he sign professional forms for Arsenal?

3 Against which side did David make his League debut?

4 And in which season?

5 How many times did David represent the England Under-21 side?

6 In which year did he win the Arsenal Player of the Year trophy?

7 Who did he score against in the last minute of the semi-final that put Arsenal through to the final of the Littlewoods Cup in 1987?

8 David was an ever present when Arsenal won the First Division Championship of 1988/89. True or false?

9 How many times did David play for England?

10 Did he play for England in either the World Cup finals or the European Championship tournament?

11 Who was the England manager throughout David's international career?

12 In which year did David leave Arsenal?

13 To which club was he transferred from Arsenal?

14 Which Third Division side was David's final League club?

15 There was a minute's silence before the match on the Saturday after David died. Who were the opposition that day?

Answers on page 179

❓ ARSENAL GREATS – IAN WRIGHT

1 In which year did Ian Wright join Arsenal?

2 From which club was he bought?

3 Who was manager of his club side before he joined Arsenal?

4 Arsenal paid a record fee for him. True or false?

5 How many League goals did Ian score in his first season at Arsenal?

6 What was his job before he became a professional footballer?

7 How many FA Cup final goals did Ian score?

8 When he became the quickest player to score 100 goals in Arsenal's history, whose 40-year-old record did he beat?

9 In the European Cup Winners' Cup of 1994/95, Ian scored in every round of the competition equalling a 30-year-old record. Whose record was it?

10 How many goals did Ian score for Arsenal?

11 Whose Arsenal League goalscoring record did he beat?

12 In which year did Ian leave Arsenal?

13 To which club was he transferred?

14 How many times did Ian play for England while an Arsenal player?

15 How many goals did he score for England?

Answers on page 184

ARSENAL GREATS – DAVID SEAMAN

1 David Seaman began his professional career with Leeds United, but couldn't get first-team games due to the consistency of the first-team keeper. Who was that keeper?

2 David was transferred to Peterborough for whom he made over one hundred appearances. True or false?

3 To which Midlands team was David transferred?

4 What was the only success that he achieved with that side?

5 The following season, after David had played in every match, what happened?

6 David next joined Queens Park Rangers. Who was the manager who signed him?

7 In which year did David join Arsenal?

8 Arsenal paid a record fee for David's services. True or false?

9 What was David's first domestic honour with Arsenal?

10 How many goals did he concede in his first season at Highbury?

11 David won his international caps while at Arsenal. True or false?

12 In 1992/93 he kept Arsenal in the Coca-Cola Cup by saving three penalties in a penalty shoot-out. Who were the opposition?

13 Which England manager selected David when he made his international debut?

14 Prior to the 2001/02 season Wales keeper Jack Kelsey had made more international appearances while at Arsenal than David Seaman. True or false?

15 Who is David's goalkeeping coach at Highbury?

Answers on page 189

ARSENAL GREATS – TONY ADAMS

1 In which year and where was Tony Adams born?

2 Who were the opposition when Tony made his League debut for Arsenal?

3 Prior to the 2001/02 season how many League Championship medals had he won?

4 How many times did he represent England?

5 And how many times as captain?

6 How many Arsenal managers has Tony played under?

7 In which year was he made captain of Arsenal?

8 What is Tony's middle name?

9 What position does he come in the list of players with most appearances for Arsenal?

10 Has he ever played in every League game in a season?

11 In which match did he notch the final goal when Arsenal completed the Double?

12 How many times did he play for the England Under-21 side?

13 Is Tony the most successful skipper in Arsenal's history?

14 How many goals did Tony score for England?

15 What was Tony's final match for England?

Answers on page 150

ARSENAL GREATS – ALAN SMITH

1 In which 'movie star' town was Alan Smith born?

2 From which club did Arsenal sign Alan?

3 In which year did Alan join Arsenal?

4 What was unusual about this transfer?

5 What did Alan achieve in his fourth League match for Arsenal?

6 How many goals did he score in his first season with Arsenal (League, Cup and League Cup goals)?

7 Which final did Arsenal reach in Alan's first season?

8 What was the first major trophy Alan won with Arsenal?

9 What was his goal tally for that season?

10 Where did Alan make his England debut during 1988/89?

11 What was unusual about his England appearances?

12 How many England managers did Alan play under?

13 How many major trophies did he win with Arsenal?

14 And how many goals did he notch up for Arsenal (League, Cup, League Cup and European goals)?

(a) 90 goals

(b) 101 goals

(c) 115 goals

15 Alan was transferred to which club at the end of his Arsenal career?

Answers on page 155

ARSENAL GREATS – LEE DIXON

1 From which club did Arsenal sign Lee Dixon?

2 Who was the manager and former England international who sold Lee Dixon to Arsenal?

3 Which team-mate followed Lee to Arsenal six months later?

4 With which northern club did Lee start his professional career?

5 Which Arsenal manager signed Lee?

6 Lee was signed for a bargain five-figure sum. True or false?

7 What was the first major trophy he won with Arsenal?

8 What is Lee's middle name?

9 Who provided the opposition for Lee's testimonial?

10 In that testimonial match which ex-Gunner star made a guest appearance?

11 Lee was sent off at Wembley in which important match?

12 How many times has he represented England?

13 How many goals has he scored for his country?

14 Who was the England manager who first chose Lee to represent his country?

15 What was unique about Lee's appearance in the 2001 FA Cup final?

Answers on page 160

ARSENAL GREATS – DENNIS BERGKAMP

1 In which city was Dennis Bergkamp born?

2 In which season did he make his Premier League debut?

3 Which Arsenal manager bought Dennis?

4 From which club did Arsenal buy him?

5 Why does Dennis usually miss European away matches?

6 What major signing did Arsenal make a month after signing Dennis?

7 How many times did Dennis play for Holland?

8 Which great player was Dennis named after?

9 Dennis scored in both legs when Holland pipped England to qualify for the 1994 World Cup finals. True or false?

10 What Dutch record does he hold?

11 How many European medals has he won?

12 What award did Dennis win in 1997/98?

13 And what award was presented to him in 1998?

14 Prior to the 2001/02 season how many honours had Dennis won with Arsenal?

15 Why didn't Dennis win an FA Cup winner's medal in 1998?

Answers on page 165

ARSENAL GREATS – THIERRY HENRY

1 Thierry was born in Paris. True or false?

2 From which club did Arsenal buy Thierry?

3 For which club had he originally played?

4 Thierry was a product of which famous football coaching school?

5 Against which club did he make his Arsenal debut?

6 And in which season?

7 What number does Thierry wear on his Arsenal shirt?

8 Thierry played in the French World Cup-winning side of 1998. True or false?

9 Prior to the 2001/02 season he jointly held which Premier League record?

10 Against which team did he score the great 'over his shoulder' volleyed goal in 2000?

11 How many League goals did Thierry score in his first season at Arsenal?

12 Prior to the 2001/02 season, how many times had he represented France at football?

13 And how many goals had he scored?

14 In the Champions League what did Thierry do that no other Gunner managed in season 2000/01?

15 Thierry plays with his socks over his knees because he likes keeping his legs warm. True or false?

Answers on page 170

THE MANAGERS – HERBERT CHAPMAN

1 In which county was Chapman born?

2 His first managerial job was as player-manager of which club?

3 After a brief spell with Leeds City, Herbert temporarily left and reverted to his original trade. What was it?

4 On returning to football, he achieved success with which club?

5 In which year did he join Arsenal?

6 What was the first major trophy Arsenal won under Chapman's guidance?

7 Who did they defeat and by what score?

8 Apart from being their first table-topping success, what was unique about Arsenal winning the Championship trophy in 1931?

9 During his successful Highbury reign which two players did Chapman choose as club captains?

10 What was the most embarrassing defeat Arsenal suffered under Chapman?

11 How many major honours did Arsenal win under his managerial guidance?

12 What were they?

13 In which year did Herbert Chapman sadly die?

14 After Chapman's death which member of staff managed the club till the end of that season?

15 Herbert Chapman once played for Tottenham Hotspur. True or false?

Answers on page 175

❓ THE MANAGERS – TOM WHITTAKER

1 Where was Tom Whittaker born?

2 What was his profession before joining Arsenal?

3 Although he spent most of his Arsenal career as a midfielder, in which position did he make his debut?

4 In which year was he promoted to first-team trainer?

5 He was awarded an MBE for his wartime services. What did he do?

6 In 1946 he was appointed as Arsenal's assistant manager. Who was the manager at that time?

7 What was Tom's full title when he became Arsenal boss?

8 And in which year was he appointed to that position?

9 How long did it take Tom to achieve his first managerial success?

10 Who was his first major signing?

11 Which giant overseas football club offered Tom Whittaker a blank contract to join them?

12 During the 1950s what major honours did Arsenal win under Whittaker's management?

13 Who were the last two players he signed for the club?

14 In which year did Tom Whittaker die?

15 What is the similarity between the deaths of Tom Whittaker and Herbert Chapman?

Answers on page 180

QUESTIONS

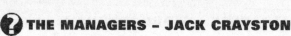

? THE MANAGERS – JACK CRAYSTON

1 What was Jack Crayston's role at Highbury before his appointment as manager?

2 In which month and year was he installed as manager of Arsenal?

3 How did Arsenal break with convention when they appointed Jack?

4 As a player with Arsenal, Jack won every honour in the game. True or false?

5 Which striker scored 25 League goals in Jack's first season as manager?

6 In Jack's first year in office, Arsenal progressed to the sixth round of the FA Cup. Which team beat them in the replay?

7 Jack introduced a youngster into League football. He is still employed looking after the manager's interests. Who is he?

8 Which poignant match took place during Jack's reign?

9 A young goalkeeper made his League debut during Jack's final season at Highbury. Name him.

10 Which international player did Jack appoint as captain in January 1958?

11 What was the highest position Arsenal finished in the League during Jack's managerial days?

12 Who took over the secretarial duties when Jack became manager in 1956?

13 Which defeat in the Cup had a strong bearing on Jack Crayston's future position as Arsenal manager?

14 How many years' service did Jack Crayston give Arsenal?

15 Which club did he join after leaving Highbury?

Answers on page 184

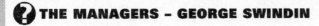

THE MANAGERS – GEORGE SWINDIN

1 With which League club did George Swindin begin his professional career?

2 In which year did he join Arsenal as a player?

3 How many medals did he win during his Highbury playing days?

4 He was granted a free transfer by Arsenal to become the player-manager of which non-League team?

5 George played only two matches for England. True or false?

6 In which year did George become the manager of Arsenal?

7 George carried on what Arsenal managerial tradition?

8 For his first signing, he went north to recruit which influential First Division Scottish defender?

9 In George's first full season in charge (1958/59) in what position did Arsenal finish in the League?

10 In that season George Swindin signed which young Irishman who would make over 250 appearances for the club?

11 In 1960/61 Arsenal were involved in the most sensational transfer deal in League history. Who did they sign?

12 What was significant about this transfer?

13 Why was that season difficult for George Swindin in general and Arsenal Football Club in particular?

14 In which year did George resign as Arsenal boss?

15 Which club did he join as manager on leaving Highbury?

Answers on page 189

QUESTIONS

THE MANAGERS – BILLY WRIGHT

1 In which year did Billy Wright become Arsenal manager?

2 What civil honour was given to him?

3 For which team did Billy Wright play?

4 What international record did he set?

5 Who was his first major signing at Arsenal?

6 At Arsenal, Billy managed a player whom he had played with both at Wolverhampton and England. Who was he?

7 In 1963 Billy signed which Scottish international central defender to shore up a leaky defence?

8 In Billy's first two seasons as manager Arsenal were defeated by the same side in the FA Cup. Who were they?

9 Which European competition did Arsenal enter for the first time during Billy's managerial stint?

10 In 1964/65 Arsenal suffered a humiliating defeat in the fourth round of the FA Cup. Who beat them?

11 Which future Arsenal manager did Billy sign?

12 What Arsenal tradition was broken during Billy's reign?

13 Billy's middle name was Ambrose. True or false?

14 Who was Billy's famous wife?

15 What footballing event took place in the summer after Billy left Highbury?

Answers on page 150

 THE MANAGERS – BERTIE MEE

1 Before Bertie Mee became Arsenal manager, what was his position at the club?

2 When Bertie first joined the club which Arsenal stalwart did he replace?

3 In which county was Bertie born?

4 When was he officially appointed Arsenal manager?

5 Name either of the League teams for which he played.

6 Who was Bertie's first big signing?

7 What was the first major final Arsenal reached under Bertie's guidance?

8 Who did Bertie employ as first-team coach?

9 Who was the Arsenal trainer during Bertie's reign?

10 At the end of the successful Double season what award did Bertie receive?

11 What civil honour was given to Bertie?

12 What was the lowest position Arsenal finished in the League under Bertie Mee?

13 Which year did Bertie Mee leave Arsenal?

14 After a short rest which club did Bertie join?

15 In which capacity did he join that club?

Answers on page 155

❓ THE MANAGERS – TERRY NEILL

1 From which club did Terry Neill join Arsenal as a player?

2 How many caps did he gain as an Irish international while at Arsenal?

3 When he left Arsenal which club did he join?

4 Who was his first assistant manager?

5 Of which club was Terry manager prior to joining Arsenal?

6 Who was his first major signing at Arsenal?

7 Which two key signings did he make from White Hart Lane?

8 How many finals did Arsenal reach during Terry's managerial reign?

9 During Terry's management Arsenal lost which two influential Irish stars?

10 What was Arsenal's highest League position while Terry was in charge?

11 Who was the expensive player Terry bought and sold without playing him?

12 Against which opponents did Arsenal suffer a disastrous home League Cup result in November 1983?

13 Which top striker did Terry sign from a German team?

14 Who was Terry's last expensive signing for Arsenal?

15 Apart from player and manager, what other position did Terry Neill hold in football?

Answers on page 161

❓ THE MANAGERS – DON HOWE

1 What was Don Howe's position at Arsenal immediately after the departure of Terry Neill in December 1983?

2 When was Don officially confirmed as Arsenal manager?

3 Don started his League career with West Bromwich Albion after a short stint at his hometown club Wolverhampton Wanderers. True or false?

4 In which year did Don join Arsenal as a player?

5 Who was the manager who signed him?

6 How many League matches did Don play for Arsenal: (a) 46 (b) 70 (c) 91?

7 What finished Don's League career?

8 What honours did he help bring to Highbury during his first spell as Arsenal coach?

9 Don left Highbury to become the manager of which club?

10 He returned to Arsenal in 1977. How many major finals did he coach the Gunners to in that second spell under manager Terry Neill?

11 During Don's stint as Arsenal manager he signed which three England international stars?

12 What was Arsenal's highest League position while Don was in charge?

13 When Don resigned as Arsenal manager in March 1986, who saw out the remainder of the season?

14 Which five England managers took advantage of Don's coaching skills?

15 What is Don Howe's current official position at Highbury (season 2001/02)?

Answers on page 166

THE MANAGERS – DON HOWE

QUESTIONS

81

❓ THE MANAGERS – GEORGE GRAHAM

1 With which club did George Graham begin his professional career?

2 Aston Villa, Chelsea, Arsenal, Manchester United, . . . , and Crystal Palace. Fill in the gap.

3 What was George's nickname during his playing days?

4 Name the first two clubs he coached before he became a manager.

5 Which manager did Arsenal approach before they appointed George?

6 Who was George's first major signing for Arsenal?

7 Who was George's first assistant manager at Arsenal?

8 A striker and a full-back who were to play a considerable part in Arsenal's success were both signed at the tail end of George's first season, 1986/87. Name them.

9 Which trophy did Arsenal win for the first time in their history under George Graham?

10 In the 1990/91 Championship success what League record did Arsenal break (for a 38-match season)?

11 Who was the last player George signed for Arsenal?

12 How many major trophies did Arsenal win during George's term as manager?

13 What was the lowest position Arsenal finished in the League under George Graham?

14 In which year did he leave Highbury?

15 Which club did he join after leaving Highbury?

Answers on page 171

THE MANAGERS – BRUCE RIOCH

1 Who was caretaker manager between George Graham's departure and Bruce Rioch's appointment?

2 Who was Arsenal's first choice for their manager?

3 From which club did Bruce join Arsenal?

4 Arsenal also enquired about his assistant. Who was he?

5 How did Arsenal break with convention when they employed Bruce Rioch?

6 In 1995 Bruce bought Dennis Bergkamp and David Platt from which two overseas clubs?

7 Arsenal progressed to the semi-final of the Coca-Cola Cup in 1996. Which team beat them on the away-goal rule?

8 With which club did Bruce begin his League career?

9 His first boss had been connected with Arsenal in a coaching capacity in the 1950s. Who was he?

10 In 1969 Bruce was transferred to which Midlands side, struggling to regain past glories?

11 And who was that club's flamboyant manager?

12 Bruce gained only one major honour during his playing career. What was it?

13 Torquay, Middlesbrough, . . . , Bolton. Fill in the gap.

14 For which country did Bruce play international football?

15 In what position did Arsenal finish in the League in Bruce Rioch's only Highbury season of 1995/96?

Answers on page 176

THE MANAGERS – ARSÈNE WENGER

1 For which clubs did Arsène Wenger play?

2 From which Japanese club did he join Arsenal?

3 Which rival manager, who played under Wenger in France, credits Arsène as his great mentor?

4 Arsène Wenger has a degree in which subject?

5 How many honours had he won before arriving at Highbury?

6 On arriving at Highbury Arsène immediately confirmed who as his assistant?

7 What revolutionary health ideas did Arsène Wenger introduce to his players?

8 In Arsène's first season at Highbury (1996/97), in what position did Arsenal finish in the Premier League?

9 Who was Arsène Wenger's first-team coach at Highbury?

10 Three of Arsène Wenger's early signings were a Dutchman and two French stars. Who were they?

11 On 14 March 1998 Arsenal clinched a famous away victory on their surge to the title. Against whom?

12 What record did Arsène set in winning the Double in 1998?

13 What award did he win at the end of the Double–winning season?

14 Who did he promote to position of kit manager?

15 Which six languages can Arsène speak fluently?

Answers on page 180

❓ MANAGING AFTER THE GUNNERS – PART 1

Name the clubs the following Arsenal players managed after leaving Highbury.

1 Alan Ball

2 David Platt

3 Joe Mercer

4 Dave Bowen

5 Eddie Hapgood

6 Terry Neill

7 Brian Talbot

8 John Radford

9 Ted Drake

10 Don Howe

11 John Barnwell

12 George Eastham

13 Freddie Cox

14 Graham Rix

15 Ronnie Rooke

Answers on page 185

MANAGING AFTER THE GUNNERS – PART 2

Name the clubs the following Arsenal players managed after leaving Highbury.

1 George Swindin

2 Viv Anderson

3 Bill Dodgin

4 Laurie Brown

5 Liam Brady

6 Tom Parker

7 Ian Ure

8 George Graham

9 Arfon Griffiths

10 Colin Addison

11 Tommy Docherty

12 Gerry Ward

13 Archie Macauley

14 David O'Leary

15 Tommy Lawton

Answers on page 189

 CHAMPIONSHIP SEASONS – 1930/31

1 What three records did Arsenal set in winning their first Championship? Record One.

2 Record Two.

3 Record Three.

4 Who was captain of Arsenal during that season?

5 Who was the season's leading goalscorer?

6 How many League goals did he score?

7 Only one player appeared in every League match that season. True or false?

8 How many League matches did Arsenal lose that season?

9 Who played in goal for the first 12 matches of the season then never played again for Arsenal?

10 At which ground in the Midlands did Arsenal play a League match in front of a crowd of 60,997?

11 Who made his debut during that season, went on to play in another two matches and finished his Arsenal career with over 300 appearances to his name?

12 What was Arsenal's biggest victory that season?

13 Who defeated Arsenal in the FA Cup that season?

14 Arsenal scored seven goals on two occasions during the season. Name their two opponents.

15 The Arsenal reserves won their championship that season. What was their league called?

Answers on page 150

CHAMPIONSHIP SEASONS – 1932/33

1 In 1932/33 Arsenal finished as champions for the second time in three years. Where did they finish in the League the previous season?

2 Arsenal conceded a mere six points in the first half of the season. True or false?

3 Arsenal scored nine goals against Sheffield Wednesday that season, with two players scoring eight of them between them. Who were that pair?

4 How many goals did Arsenal score during the season?

5 Which Arsenal stalwart made his final five League appearances for the club at the start of the season?

6 Who finished as runners-up to Arsenal that season?

7 Arsenal scored eight League goals or more in a match on three occasions. True or false?

8 Who was the season's leading goalscorer?

9 Arsenal had three men sent off in a single match. True or false?

10 Frank Moss played in goal for all but one of the Championship League matches. Who was between the posts for that one game?

11 Who scored his only goal in the final League match of the season?

12 Arsenal suffered arguably their worst FA Cup defeat that season. Who were the opposition?

13 An Arsenal player made his only appearance for the club in that FA Cup defeat. Due to a show of petulance he was sent off, transfer listed and sold. Who was he?

14 How many Arsenal players made international appearances during the season?

15 Who scored three times in only four League appearances for Arsenal?

Answers on page 155

❓ CHAMPIONSHIP SEASONS – 1933/34

1 Which two managers were in charge of Arsenal during 1933/34?

2 Who was Arsenal's captain that season?

3 On only two occasions did Arsenal score more than three goals in a game in 1933/34. True or false?

4 Who did Arsenal play in the Charity Shield that season and what was the score?

5 An Arsenal 'great' was purchased during that season. Name him?

6 Two players tied as the season's leading scorers. Who were they?

7 Arsenal's ground attendance record was beaten twice during the season. What was the crowd figure for the second match?

8 Who was the Arsenal goalkeeper who played in 37 League matches that season?

9 Which Irish international star was signed from Sheffield United in September 1933?

10 An Arsenal defender was the only player to play in every League match that season. Who was he?

11 Arsenal's biggest win that season was not in their League campaign but in the FA Cup. Who did they defeat and by what score?

12 Who beat Arsenal in the quarter-finals of the FA Cup?

13 Who was the promising half-back who made his single League appearance for the senior side that season?

14 Arsenal did not beat Spurs once that season. True or false?

15 Surprisingly, Arsenal had only three capped players that season, and they were all English internationals. Name them.

Answers on page 161

CHAMPIONSHIP SEASONS – 1933/34

CHAMPIONSHIP SEASONS - 1934/35

1 Which manager was in charge of Arsenal in 1934/35?

2 Which four great Arsenal servants had left the club before the start of the season?

3 Two of the replacements were to become Arsenal legends. Name them.

4 Arsenal broke their attendance record during the season. What was the new figure (that still stands) and who were the opponents?

5 Whose record were Arsenal attempting to equal in the quest for their third consecutive Championship?

6 Arsenal demolished Spurs both home and away that season. What were the scores?

7 Who defeated Arsenal in the FA Cup that season?

8 Arsenal scored eight times in three League matches that season. True or false?

9 In the final match of that Championship season a young full-back made his only League appearance for Arsenal. Who was he?

10 What rare feat did regular keeper Frank Moss achieve that season?

11 Who broke Arsenal's goalscoring record that season and still holds that record?

12 How many times did he find the back of the net?

13 No one played in every League match that Championship season. True or false?

14 Who were relegated that season after finishing bottom of the First Division?

15 In recognition of their third consecutive Championship what did the Football League present to the club?

Answers on page 166

❓ CHAMPIONSHIP SEASONS - 1937/38

1 Name the manager who guided Arsenal to the Championship in 1937/38.

2 Which two teams defeated Arsenal at Highbury during the Championship season.

3 Alex Wilson and George Swindin started and finished in goal that season, but which other keeper played between the posts?

4 The largest crowd for an Arsenal match that season was 75,952. Where was it and who were the opposition?

5 Which Arsenal star played in the first 13 League matches then did not make another appearance for the rest of the season?

6 Who was Arsenal's top League goalscorer that season?

7 How many League goals did he score?

8 Which team finished as runners-up to Arsenal that season?

9 Who defeated Arsenal in the FA Cup that season?

10 No Arsenal player played in every Championship game that season. True or false?

11 Arsenal's largest crowd at Highbury that season was 68,353. Who were the opposition that day?

12 A future prolific Arsenal goalscorer made his debut during the season and scored. Name him.

13 What was Arsenal's biggest winning margin that season?

14 Who was the great wing-forward who left Arsenal in January 1938?

15 Who did Arsenal qualify to play in the Charity Shield the following season?

Answers on page 171

CHAMPIONSHIP SEASONS – 1947/48

1 How many consecutive games did Arsenal play without defeat from the start of 1947/48?

2 Who were the first side to beat Arsenal that season?

3 Who was Arsenal's top League goalscorer that season?

4 Arsenal set a new record for the fewest goals conceded in a First Division season. How many goals did they concede?

5 The largest Championship crowd Arsenal played in front of that season was 81,962. Who were the opposition?

6 Where was that match played?

7 Arsenal equalled the record for the fewest players used in a League Division One season. How many players did they use?

8 Two players appeared in every League match that season. Who were they?

9 Who started in the first six League matches but did not play again for the rest of the season?

10 Ronnie Rooke was the regular penalty-taker that season but another Arsenal star scored from the spot, even though Rooke was playing in the match. Who was he?

11 During the season Arsenal played a friendly match at Highbury against a side that did not gain League status for another two seasons. Who was that?

12 Which player from the Chapman era made his final League appearance for Arsenal that season?

13 An international defender was signed during the second half of the season and played in 11 matches of the Championship run-in. Name him.

14 Which Arsenal player, who would gain 22 full caps for his country, made his international debut that season?

15 There was a shock in store for the all-conquering Arsenal side in the FA Cup that season. Who defeated them and by what score?

Answers on page 176

 CHAMPIONSHIP SEASONS – 1970/71

1 Who was Arsenal's Double-winning skipper in 1971?

2 How many matches did Arsenal play to win the FA Cup?

3 Where was the first semi-final played?

4 Where was the semi-final replay played?

5 Who scored the Championship-winning goal against Spurs?

6 On which day of the week was that match against Spurs played?

7 Who knocked Arsenal out of the League Cup that season?

8 How many matches did Arsenal lose at home during the season?

9 How many league goals did Arsenal concede at home during the season?

10 Name the three players who played in every match throughout the Double-winning season.

11 Who defeated Arsenal in the European Fairs Cup that season?

12 Who scored the last-minute penalty to salvage the first semi-final?

13 By how many points did Arsenal finish above second-place Leeds United?

14 Name Arsenal's reserve goalkeeper throughout the season.

15 Which player played in only three matches throughout the Double-winning season but was to finish with over 324 appearances for Arsenal throughout his Highbury career?

Answers on page 180

CHAMPIONSHIP SEASONS – 1988/89

1 Who was Arsenal's Championship skipper in 1989?

2 Who scored a hat-trick in the first League match of the season?

3 Who made his Arsenal debut in that first match?

4 What was Arsenal's biggest attendance that season?

5 Who were Arsenal's opponents in that match?

6 Which former Everton player scored a goal in Arsenal's win at Goodison Park?

7 Which three players completed every match that season?

8 Who was the season's leading scorer?

9 Which leggy Irishman made two League appearances that season?

10 Who defeated Arsenal in the FA Cup that season?

11 In the second replay of the League Cup Arsenal lost to which side?

12 That deciding match was played on a neutral ground. Where was it?

13 Who scored the goal that brought the Championship to Highbury?

14 Who was the beaten Liverpool keeper?

15 What was so significant about that goal?

Answers on page 185

 CHAMPIONSHIP SEASONS – 1990/91

1 Who were Arsenal's three new major signings?

2 Name the manager who guided Arsenal to the title.

3 Which two players made only one substitute appearance each during the season?

4 Who was the season's leading goalscorer?

5 Who were Arsenal's opponents at the only match the Gunners lost that season?

6 What was the final score?

7 The Football League deducted two points from Arsenal for events at which match?

8 What happened at that match?

9 Which four players played in every match of that Championship season?

10 For a period of that season Alan Smith went 11 matches without scoring. True or false?

11 Who thrashed Arsenal in that season's League Cup and what was the score?

12 Who defeated Arsenal in a stirring game in the FA Cup semi-final that season?

13 Where was that semi-final played?

14 By how many points did Arsenal finish clear of second-place Liverpool?

15 What European award was made to Alan Smith at the end of the season?

Answers on page 190

QUESTIONS

CHAMPIONSHIP SEASONS – 1997/98

1 Who were Arsenal's two new big-money signings?

2 From which clubs were they bought?

3 How many games did Arsenal lose during their Championship campaign?

4 Which prolific star played his final match for Arsenal that season?

5 How many games did Arsenal play before their first Premier League defeat?

6 Which team defeated them and by what score?

7 Who was the young centre-back signed in the close season who made five Premier League appearances in 1997/98?

8 Who was the foreign goalkeeper signed prior to the start of the season?

9 Who was the season's leading goalscorer?

10 How many goals did he score?

11 Who played only one match (no substitute appearances) that season?

12 Who knocked Arsenal out of the League Cup?

13 No player played in every Premier League match that season. True or false?

14 What was Arsenal's biggest victory during the season?

15 Who defeated Arsenal in the FA Cup that season?

Answers on page 151

❓ FA CUP SEMI-FINALS – PART 1

1 Who were the opponents in Arsenal's first FA Cup semi-final?

2 In the 1932 and 1936 semi-finals, the winning goals in Arsenal's 1–0 victories were scored by the same player. Name him.

3 Who did Arsenal defeat in the semi-final at Stamford Bridge in 1927?

4 Prior to 2001/02 at which ground have Arsenal played most of their semi-final matches?

5 How many times have they played there?

6 When and where did they play their first semi-final on a ground that was not owned by a League side?

7 What is the most games Arsenal have played to defeat semi-final opponents and in which year was that?

8 Who were their opponents?

9 What is Arsenal's biggest win in an FA Cup semi-final?

10 Which London sides have Arsenal played in Cup semi-finals?

11 How many times (including replays) have Arsenal played FA Cup semi-finals at London grounds?

12 Who notched up Arsenal's winner in the 1998 semi-final against Wolverhampton Wanderers?

13 Arsenal have lost seven FA Cup semi-finals. True or false?

14 How many times (including replays) have Arsenal played Manchester United in FA Cup semi-finals?

15 Prior to 2001/02, which player has scored the most goals for Arsenal in FA Cup semi-finals?

Answers on page 156

❓ FA CUP SEMI-FINALS – PART 2

1 Which central defender scored Arsenal's equalizer in the 1950 FA Cup semi-final?

2 When Bob Wilson was injured during the 1972 semi-final who replaced him in goal?

3 Name the only team Arsenal have played in the semi-finals whose name begins with 'G'.

4 Who did Arsenal beat in the semi-final on the way to their first FA Cup final?

5 What was the first FA Cup semi-final involving Arsenal to be televised live?

6 Who was the last Arsenal skipper to score in an FA Cup semi-final?

7 While Arsenal were winning their semi-final in 1978 the other semi-final was being played at Highbury. Which teams were playing?

8 Who made his sole FA Cup appearance in goal in the 1983 semi-final?

9 Name the only opposition Arsenal have faced twice in FA Cup finals in consecutive seasons.

10 In which years did they play these opponents?

11 Arsenal were once defeated by the same opposition in the semi-final stages of both the FA Cup and the Football League Cup. Name the opposition and the year.

12 Since the war, who has scored the most goals against Arsenal in an FA Cup semi-final?

13 Who was the last Arsenal player to miss a penalty in an FA Cup semi-final?

14 Which was the last club from a lower division to defeat Arsenal in an FA Cup semi-final?

15 And in which year?

Answers on page 161

DEBUTS – PART 1

Name the season these Gunners made their debuts for Arsenal.

1 John Hartson

2 Leslie Compton

3 Charlie Nicholas

4 Gordon Nutt

5 Nicolas Anelka

6 Jimmy Bloomfield

7 Robert Pires

8 George Wood

9 Alex Manninger

10 Ray Kennedy

11 Ray Parlour

12 George Swindin

13 John Lukic

14 Frank Stapleton

15 Pat Jennings

Answers on page 166

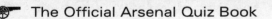

DEBUTS – PART 2

Name the season these Gunners made their debuts for Arsenal.

1 Wally Barnes
2 Bob McNab
3 Jimmy Robertson
4 Nwankwo Kanu
5 Laurie Scott
6 David Court
7 Joe Hulme
8 Jim Standen
9 Gilles Grimandi
10 Reg Lewis
11 Gerry Ward
12 Herbie Roberts
13 Marc Overmars
14 Jack Crayston
15 Paul Shaw

Answers on page 171

BEFORE THE GUNNERS – PART 1

Name the clubs from which Arsenal recruited these players.

1 Bobby Gould

2 Marc Overmars

3 Viv Anderson

4 Bernard Joy

5 Dennis Bergkamp

6 Terry Mancini

7 Perry Groves

8 Steve Bould

9 Thierry Henry

10 Joe Baker

11 Brian Kidd

12 Tommy Lawton

13 Geoff Barnett

14 Dan Lewis

15 Luis Boa Morte

Answers on page 176

QUESTIONS

? BEFORE THE GUNNERS – PART 2

Name the clubs from which Arsenal recruited these players.

1 Colin Addison

2 Emmanuel Petit

3 Tommy Catton

4 John 'Jock' Rutherford

5 Alf Baker

6 Kevin Richardson

7 Laurie Brown

8 Silvinho

9 Jeff Blockley

10 Bob McNab

11 Jimmy Carter

12 Lee Chapman

13 Siggi Jonsson

14 Alf Common

15 David Herd

Answers on page 181

❓ BEFORE THE GUNNERS - PART 3

Name the clubs from which Arsenal recruited these players.

1 Lauren
2 Alan Smith
3 Willie Young
4 Mike Tiddy
5 Jim Furnell
6 Steve Williams
7 Oleg Luzhny
8 Stefan Schwarz
9 Alan Sunderland
10 Patrick Vieira
11 Alex Cropley
12 Jack Crayston
13 Alan Ball
14 Ted Drake
15 Tommy Docherty

Answers on page 185

• BEFORE THE GUNNERS – PART 3

The Official Arsenal Quiz Book

❓ CAPITAL GUNNERS – PART 1

These Arsenal stars were involved with other London clubs. Who are they?

1 This defender was once manager of Queens Park Rangers.

2 He toured most of the London sides after a 'non-playing' career at Highbury.

3 A 'young pretender' who lists Orient and Barnet among the clubs for which he played after his Highbury days.

4 He gained a winning medal in 1967 with another capital side.

5 A pre-war superstar who managed Arsenal's North London rivals.

6 He was transferred from another North London side and gained an FA Cup winner's medal with his new team.

7 He played in a 1960s FA Cup final and later also managed a West London outfit.

8 He was arguably both North London clubs' greatest keeper.

9 He played for Brentford and Orient.

10 This striker was purchased from Tottenham Hotspur in 1937.

11 He played for both North London giants in the late 1940s.

12 During his career he was manager of Brentford and assistant manager at Millwall.

13 An England striker who managed Fulham in 1980.

14 He played at West Ham United in 1987 before coaching at Wimbledon.

15 An Irish international keeper of the 1960s who also guarded the goal at Fulham.

Answers on page 190

CAPITAL GUNNERS – PART 2

These Arsenal stars were involved with other London clubs. Who are they?

1 A Double-winning striker who also played for West Ham United.

2 Portsmouth, Wolverhampton Wanderers, Arsenal and Fulham were this player's professional clubs.

3 After starring in over 150 matches for Arsenal, he went to the 'Palace' at the start of the 1980s.

4 A star of the 1950s who lists Charlton, Orient and Crystal Palace among the clubs he scored for after his gunning days.

5 He scored an FA Cup-winning goal for Arsenal and was later transferred to Crystal Palace.

6 A Scottish Double-winner transferred to South Africa Road.

7 He was bought by Arsenal from Crystal Palace shortly after the war to score goals and he won a Championship.

8 This promising keeper became a 'Cottager' in 1969.

9 He went to play beside the Thames in 1977 after winning everything at Highbury.

10 An Arsenal Scottish international multi-trophy winner who joined Leyton Orient on a free transfer in 1956.

11 The 'right man', especially before joining West Ham.

12 An Arsenal forward who was transferred to a West London Club where he won an FA Cup winner's medal in 1970.

13 An Irish international defender transferred to Millwall in 1966.

14 A mega-star who played for many teams either side of the war including Chelsea and Brentford before joining Arsenal.

15 Tottenham Hotspur, Arsenal and Nottingham Forest were some of his clubs.

Answers on page 151

CAPITAL GUNNERS – PART 2

QUESTIONS

❓❓❓❓❓❓❓❓❓❓ **105**

? THE NAME GAME – EXTRA

These soccer stars share their surnames with Arsenal players, past and present. Name both players.

1 West Ham United and England central defender, who also managed Norwich City.

2 World Cup winner from Liverpool.

3 The 'Golden Vision'.

4 Wolves and England keeper from the 1940s/1950s.

5 From Wimbledon to Hollywood.

6 Young petulant Leeds striker.

7 Watford, Liverpool and England striker who tried management at Celtic.

8 The 'Toon' resurrected.

9 Manchester United and England striker, sadly lost at Munich.

10 West Ham and England's custodian.

11 Ex-Brighton boss now at Leicester.

12 Manchester United and England's glittering knight.

13 The 'Number Three' in Spurs Double side.

14 Villa's winning skipper in the 1957 FA Cup final.

15 The 'wizard of the dribble'.

Answers on page 156

NATIVE COUNTRIES – PART 1

In which countries were these Gunners past and present born?

1 Kwame Ampadu

2 John Kosmina

3 Siggi Jonsson

4 Anders Limpar

5 Kaba Diawara

6 Gerry Keyser

7 David Grondin

8 Fabian Caballero

9 Daniel Le Roux

10 Glenn Helder

11 Chris Kiwomya

12 Albert Gudmundsson

13 Nwankwo Kanu

14 John Jensen

15 Brendon Batson

Answers on page 162

NATIVE COUNTRIES – PART 2

NATIVE COUNTRIES – PART 2

In which countries were these Gunners past and present born?

1 Oleg Luzhny

2 Charlie Preedy

3 Jehad Muntasser

4 Alex Manninger

5 Davor Suker

6 Paolo Vernazza

7 Pal Lydersen

8 Nelson Vivas

9 Christopher Wreh

10 Omer Riza

11 Vladimir Petrovic

12 Silvinho

13 Paul Vaessen

14 Stefan Schwarz

15 Alberto Mendez

Answers on page 167

CLUB NICKNAMES

Give the nicknames of these clubs that faced Arsenal in 2000/01?

1 Liverpool

2 Charlton Athletic

3 Coventry City

4 Carlisle United

5 Aston Villa

6 Manchester City

7 Derby County

8 Southampton

9 Newcastle United

10 Leicester City

11 Sunderland

12 Queens Park Rangers

13 Bradford City

14 Ipswich Town

15 Blackburn Rovers

Answers on page 172

QUESTIONS

MULTIPLE CHOICE – PART 1

1 Who played the most games for Arsenal:
(a) Frank McLintock (b) Kenny Sansom (c) Steve Bould?

2 Who was an international player before he joined Arsenal:
(a) Ted Drake (b) Bob McNab (c) Ian Wright?

3 Who scored the most League goals for Arsenal:
(a) Joe Baker (b) Frank Stapleton (c) Tony Woodcock?

4 Who joined Arsenal first:
(a) Nigel Winterburn (b) David Seaman (c) Alan Smith?

5 Which manager was at Highbury for the shortest time?
(a) Don Howe (b) Jack Crayston (c) Bruce Rioch?

6 Which Arsenal star was born the furthest north:
(a) David Seaman (b) Ray Kennedy (c) Lee Dixon?

7 Which club has Arsenal played the most times in the old
League: (a) Nottingham Forest (b) Wolverhampton Wanderers
(c) Bolton Wanderers?

8 Who was the smallest player:
(a) Alex James (b) Alan Ball (c) Paul Dickov?

9 Prior to season 2000/01 which team have Arsenal defeated
most times in the Premier League: (a) Chelsea (b) Newcastle
United (c) Leeds United?

10 Name the only Arsenal player to have won a trophy with the
club: (a) Terry Neill (b)Tony Woodcock (c) John Jensen?

11 Which Arsenal player has won the most international caps: (a)
Viv Anderson (b) Steve Morrow (c) Pal Lydersen?

12 Which Arsenal star played the most times during their 1997/98
Double-winning season: (a) Christopher Wreh (b) John
Roberts (c) Luis Boa Morte?

13 Who won the most trophies during his stay at Highbury:
(a) Peter Goring (b) Jon Sammels (c) David Rocastle?

14 Which team have Arsenal never played in the Charity Shield:
(a) West Bromwich Albion (b) Cardiff City (c) Sunderland?

15 Whose nickname is 'Rodders': (a) Ray Parlour
(b) Rodney Smithson (c) Tony Adams?

Answers on page 177

❓ MULTIPLE CHOICE – PART 2

1 Who played for the most Football League clubs:
(a) Kenny Sansom (b) Tommy Lawton (c) Trevor Ross?

2 Who was an Arsenal player for the longest period:
(a) Eddie Hapgood (b) Peter Storey (c) Pat Rice?

3 Which of these Arsenal players was not born in London:
(a) Andy Cole (b) David O'Leary (c) Ian Wright?

4 Which club have Arsenal not played in the FA Youth Cup final:
(a) Millwall (b) Chelsea (c) Everton?

5 Who was never a caretaker boss at Arsenal:
(a) Steve Burkenshaw b) Theo Foley c) Don Howe?

6 Who was the Arsenal secretary in 2001:
a) Daniel Fiszman (b) David Miles (c) Ken Friar?

7 Which of the following Arsenal defenders is the tallest:
(a) Herbie Roberts (b) Willie Young (c) Leslie Compton?

8 Which sponsored section of the League Cup have Arsenal
never won: (a) The Milk Cup (b) The Littlewoods Cup
(c) The Coca-Cola Cup?

9 Prior to 2000/01 which team have Arsenal played the most
times in the Premier League:
(a) Queens Park Rangers (b) Bradford City (b) Watford?

10 Which Arsenal player has not played for Tottenham Hotspur:
(a) Steve Walford (b) George Hunt (c) George Cox?

11 Which French team has Robert Pires not played for:
(a) Stade de Reims (b) AS Monaco (c) Olympique Marseille?

12 In which European Cup Winners' Cup final did Arsenal not
play in their traditional red and white shirts:
(a) The 1980 final (b) The 1994 final (c) The 1995 final?

13 Which manager was in charge at Arsenal the longest:
(a) George Graham (b) Bertie Mee (c) Herbert Chapman?

14 In 1950 what was the price of the *Official Arsenal Handbook*:
(a) Sixpence (b) One shilling (c) One shilling and sixpence?

15 In which season were Arsenal last relegated to Division Two?
(a) 1908/09 (b) 1912/13 (c) 1921/22?

Answers on page 181

QUESTIONS

GREAT GAMES – V NEWCASTLE, 1952 FA CUP FINAL

1 This was the first time Arsenal had met Newcastle United in an FA Cup final at Wembley. True or false?

2 The Double eluded Arsenal that season. Where did they finish in the League?

3 One of Arsenal's star defenders was given permission by the FA to play with a cast protecting a broken arm. Who was he?

4 Who had been discharged from hospital to play in the final?

5 Where was Arsenal's FA Cup semi-final played that season?

6 Who were the opposition?

7 Who made only one appearance during Arsenal's run to the final?

8 Eight of the Cup final team had played in every match up to the final. Name the three who did not.

9 Which Arsenal star injured himself so badly that he took no further part in the final?

10 Which forward was asked to drop back to bridge the defensive gap?

11 How long were Arsenal required to hold out with only ten men?

12 With 11 minutes remaining an Arsenal forward struck the Newcastle bar. Who was he?

13 Who scored the last-gasp winning goal for Newcastle United?

14 In winning the Cup what twentieth-century record did Newcastle set?

15 Who said, 'I thought football's greatest honour was representing your country. I was wrong, it was playing for Arsenal today'?

Answers on page 186

GREAT GAMES – V MANCHESTER UNITED, FEBRUARY 1958

1 What was the final score in that phenomenal match?

2 To the nearest thousand, guess the attendance.

3 Who had been promoted to Arsenal skipper in the weeks prior to the fixture?

4 What was the score at half-time?

5 Who scored two goals for Arsenal during that game?

6 What was Arsenal's League placing at the end of that season?

7 A young striker had just forced his way into the United set-up. Name him.

8 Who was the Arsenal striker that day who would join Manchester United three seasons later?

9 What had been the result at Old Trafford earlier in the season?

10 Manchester United returned to Highbury later in the season. What was the fixture?

11 And what was the score?

12 A young Manchester United star was booked during that match for a heavy tackle on Arsenal's Dennis Evans. In later years Dennis regretted that he had not retaliated and stopped that player from going on the following week's fateful trip to Munich. Who was the player involved?

13 Who was in charge of Manchester United for the match?

14 Who was Arsenal's boss?

15 It would be another 12 years before Arsenal won another major trophy. What was that honour?

Answers on page 190

GREAT GAMES – V ANDERLECHT, 1970 FAIRS CUP FINAL

1 Who had Arsenal defeated in their semi-final?

2 Name the superstar who had played against Arsenal in the semi-final.

3 What was the aggregate score that saw Arsenal through to the final?

4 Who was the only substitute used in the two matches?

5 What was the full name of the ground where the first leg was played?

6 What was the score after the first leg in Brussels?

7 Who snatched the 'priceless' away goal for Arsenal in the first leg?

8 Which manager guided Arsenal to their success?

9 How long was it since Arsenal had last won a major trophy?

10 Who scored the important first goal?

11 What was the score at half-time in the second leg?

12 Who scored the goal that brought the European trophy to Highbury?

13 On which day of the week was the second leg at Highbury played?

14 To the nearest thousand, what was the attendance at Highbury?

15 Which member of that Cup-winning side left Arsenal just over a year later?

Answers on page 151

GREAT GAMES – V SPURS, MAY 1971

1 What was the importance of this match?

2 What result would have stopped Arsenal's successful surge to glory?

3 Who were the other Championship contenders that season?

4 On which day of the week was this match played?

5 Who was the referee for that match?

6 Who said, 'Arsenal have got as much chance of being handed the title by Spurs as I have of being given the Crown Jewels'?

7 Which regular Arsenal star was injured and did not play in this match?

8 To the nearest thousand, what was the attendance?

9 Who coached the Gunners throughout that memorable season?

10 Who scored the all-important goal?

11 Did he score it with a rasping shot or a powerful header?

12 Who returned the ball into the centre for the goal?

13 When the goal was scored a Tottenham player was lying injured in the goalmouth. Who was it: (a) Knowles (b) Kinnear (c) Collins?

14 In his excitement who did Arsenal keeper Bob Wilson hug at the final whistle?

15 What consolation trophy did Tottenham win that season?

Answers on page 156

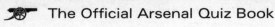
❓ ARSENAL NOW

1 What is Arsenal's postal code:
(a) N7 1BE (b) N2 7RG (c) N5 1BU?

2 What is the current price of Arsenal's matchday programme?

3 What is the name of the main merchandise shop attached to the ground?

4 Who is Arsenal's Life President?

5 What is the name of Arsenal's colourful mascot?

6 What colourful recognition does the visiting team always receive on matchdays?

7 Which mainline station is the nearest to Highbury?

8 Who is Arsenal's Chairman?

9 Who do Arsenal traditionally employ to supervise and welcome their guests on matchdays?

10 What is the nostalgic building situated in the North Bank stand?

11 Who is Arsenal's Vice Chairman?

12 What is the official capacity of Highbury?

13 Name the corporate hospitality site at Highbury that is named after an Arsenal 'great'.

14 Which member of Arsène Wenger's backroom staff is the manager of the Arsenal Ladies team?

15 What Arsenal logo was redesigned in 2002?

Answers on page 162

LEAGUE APPEARANCES

Name the club for which these Arsenal players have made the most League appearances:

1 Geoff Strong

2 Freddie Cox

3 George Wood

4 John Hawley

5 Don Howe

6 Jim Furnell

7 David Jenkins

8 Viv Anderson

9 Brian Marwood

10 John Roberts

11 Alan Ball

12 Jackie Henderson

13 Wilf Rostron

14 Jon Sammels

15 Tommy Lawton

Answers on page 167

OPPOSITION GROUNDS

Name the new ground and the old ground of the clubs listed below:

1 Bolton Wanderers

2 Northampton Town

3 Middlesbrough

4 Stoke City

5 Derby County

6 Brighton and Hove Albion

7 Southampton

8 Oxford United

9 Sunderland

10 Walsall

11 Huddersfield Town

12 Wigan Athletic

13 Wycombe Wanderers

14 Reading

15 Millwall

Answers on page 172

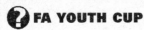

FA YOUTH CUP

1 How many times have Arsenal won the FA Youth Cup final?

2 In which seasons did they win them?

3 In which season did Arsenal lose the final for the one and only time?

4 How many times have Arsenal been eliminated at the semi-final stage of the Youth Cup: (a) twice (b) four times (c) seven times?

5 In which season was the first set of Youth Cup matches played?

6 Who was the Arsenal manager who allowed Arsenal to enter the Youth Cup competition?

7 Is the Youth Cup final decided on one match or on a two-legged home-and-away basis?

8 Which was the side Arsenal defeated to win their first final?

9 Which two players in that winning team progressed to first-team level and played in the Double-winning side of 1971?

10 Name the striker who won an FA Youth Cup winner's medal in 1978 and proceeded to League, FA Cup and League Cup success with Arsenal before being transferred to Nottingham Forest.

11 In recent years who has sponsored the FA Youth Cup?

12 Only one team has won the FA Youth Cup more times than Arsenal. Who are they?

13 Name the two sides Arsenal defeated in back-to-back FA Youth Cup finals in 1999/2000 and 2000/01.

14 Who are the two coaches behind Arsenal's recent Youth Cup successes?

15 In the 2001 Youth Cup win, which player scored nine goals during the tournament?

Answers on page 177

ARSENAL AT WAR

❓ ARSENAL AT WAR

1 The match action against Brentford in May 1939 was used for what?

2 How many League Division One matches were played during 1939/40?

3 What was the result of Arsenal's final match prior to the outbreak of World War Two?

4 What League formation did Arsenal compete in during the Second World War?

5 Arsenal played in the League War Cup final in 1940/41. Who were the opposition?

6 Where were the final and the replay played?

7 To what use was Highbury put during the Second World War?

8 After the damage to Highbury where did Arsenal play all their wartime home matches?

9 What section of Highbury was destroyed by enemy action?

10 Arsenal won the 1941/42 and 1942/43 London Leagues at a canter, scoring 108 and 101 goals in the process. Who netted a massive 42 goals in that first season?

11 Arsenal ran riot in the War Cup final of 1943. Who were their opponents and what was the score?

12 In 1944/45 Arsenal failed to beat Millwall in the semi-final at Stamford Bridge. Two penalties were missed, one by a guest forward who made a big impact in the period directly after the war with Blackpool and England. Who was he?

13 Manager Tom Whittaker and Cliff Bastin were not available for active service, but they both stayed at Highbury throughout the war. To do what?

14 Four great players from Arsenal's 'golden era' sadly suffered serious injuries during the Second World War and never played for the club again. Who were they?

15 In 1945/46, Arsenal played in a prestigious friendly against a touring side. Name that side.

Answers on page 181

❓ FA CUP APPEARANCES

Name the other club with which these Arsenal players have been FA Cup winners.

1 Michael Thomas.

2 David Herd.

3 Brian Talbot.

4 John Hollins.

5 Geoff Strong.

6 David Jack.

7 Frank Stapleton.

8 Eddie Clamp.

9 John 'Jock' Rutherford.

10 Paul Mariner.

11 Jimmy Robertson.

12 Tommy Baldwin.

13 Kevin Richardson.

14 Andy Ducat.

15 Pat Jennings.

Answers on page 186

❓ FA CUP OPPONENTS

Between 1946 and 2001 Arsenal played the following teams only once in the FA Cup. Name the season.

1 Peterborough United.

2 Colchester United.

3 Crystal Palace.

4 Bradford Park Avenue.

5 Swindon Town.

6 Hereford United.

7 Newport County.

8 Darlington.

9 Grimsby Town.

10 Walsall.

11 Plymouth Argyle.

12 Bedford Town.

13 Port Vale.

14 Doncaster Rovers.

15 Cambridge United.

Answers on page 191

THE FA CHARITY SHIELD

1 In which season did Arsenal first play in the Charity Shield?

2 What was the result of the match?

3 Where was the match played?

4 After that initial game where were the matches played before they were held at Wembley?

5 There was a wonderfully exciting match at Highbury in 1998 between Arsenal and the previous season's Cup winners. What was the score?

6 Highbury staged the Charity Shield of 1949. Who were the sides playing that day?

7 When did Arsenal first play in an FA Charity Shield at Wembley?

8 Who were their opponents that day?

9 Liverpool is the side Arsenal have met most times in the Charity Shield. True or false?

10 In which year did they play Tottenham Hotspur in the Charity Shield?

11 Who scored for Arsenal in that match?

12 An Arsenal striker who found fame with other Premier League sides made a substitute appearance in the Tottenham Charity Shield match. Who was he?

13 Arsenal played in the 1999/2000 Charity Shield even though they were neither League Champions nor FA Cup winners. Why?

14 Have Arsenal ever been involved in a penalty shoot-out to decide the result of the Charity Shield?

15 In the 2000 season which company sponsored the FA Charity Shield?

Answers on page 152

❓ THE MISSING LINK

Fill in the missing link.

1 Charlie Nicholas: Celtic, Arsenal, ..., Celtic.

2 Joe Mercer, ..., Tony Adams.

3 Crystal Palace, Arsenal, West Ham, ...

4 Frank Stapleton: 1978, 1979, ...

5 Terry Neill: FA Cup winners, FA Cup finalist, ...

6 Plumstead Common, Sportsman Ground, ... , Invicta Ground.

7 1930, 1936, ... , 1971, 1979, 1993, 1998.

8 Armstrong, Sammels, Radford, ... , Graham.

9 Jack Crayston: Bradford Park Avenue, Arsenal, ...

10 Port Vale, Middlesbrough, ... , West Ham United, Wolverhampton Wanderers, Newcastle United.

11 Joe Baker: Hibernian, Torino, Arsenal, Nottingham Forest, ...

12 West Bromwich Albion, Arsenal, Queens Park Rangers, ...

13 1970/71, ...

14 Dial Square, ... , Woolwich Arsenal, Arsenal.

15 Stade de Reims, FC Metz, ... , Arsenal.

Answers on page 157

? TRUE OR FALSE? – PART 2

1 Pat Jennings is the oldest player to appear for Arsenal.

2 Arsenal stars John Radford and Tony Adams appeared in the Youth team the season after they had made their League debuts.

3 Wimbledon tennis queen Virginia Wade is the niece of Joe Wade, Arsenal's 1950s full-back.

4 Freddie Ljungberg always dyes his hair to the standard shirt colour of the team for which he is playing.

5 Kanu once had to undergo life-threatening heart surgery.

6 Arthur 'Happy' Jinks, a goalkeeper from Arsenal's pioneering days of the 1900s, lost an arm during the Great War, but managed to play in an outfield position for the club on two occasions when the war ended.

7 An Arsenal star first played in the reserve team in 1909 but did not play in the first team until 1925, some 16 years later.

8 David Jack, one of Arsenal's all-time greats, was once left out by disciplinarian Herbert Chapman because he smoked too much.

9 Danny Le Roux played five games for Arsenal in the 1950s.

10 Tom Vallance, an Arsenal star of the 1950s, was Sir Stan Matthews' brother-in-law.

11 The author of *Fever Pitch*, Nick Hornby, is an avid fan of Arsenal after growing up less than a mile from the stadium.

12 Arsenal and England's keeper David Seaman was an accomplished cricketer and was once on the Yorkshire County Cricket Club groundstaff.

13 Arsenal's skipper of the 1950s Dave Bowen played 164 matches for the club and only scored two goals – both against Spurs, and both in the same match.

QUESTIONS

TRUE OR FALSE? – PART 2 CONT.

14 Because of the deteriorating condition of his knees, Arsenal footballer and England cricket star Denis Compton was advised by the Arsenal training staff to cycle to Highbury from his home in Hendon. He carried out their instructions to the letter towards the end of his Arsenal career.

15 Arsenal star Alex James loved a drop of the hard stuff and found himself a 'little over the top' on numerous occasions. He would demand a sea voyage to aid his recovery. Arsenal did send him to sea – but in a small, smelly fishing trawler in the Irish Sea.

Answers on page 162

ARSENAL V MANCHESTER UNITED

1 Prior to 2000/01 who had won more League matches, Arsenal or Manchester United?

2 Which club entered the Football League first, Woolwich Arsenal or Newton Heath (United)?

3 When did the clubs first play each other?

4 Who were the captains of Arsenal and Manchester United for the 1957 encounter prior to the Munich disaster?

5 In which season did Arsenal and Manchester United first clash in the FA Cup Charity Shield?

6 Since the war a Scottish striker and a Republic of Ireland striker have joined Manchester United from Arsenal and scored FA Cup final goals for United. Name them.

7 In which season did the teams play each other in the FA Cup and the League Cup?

8 In which season did Arsenal and Manchester United last play in front of a Highbury gate that exceeded 60,000?

9 Which England full-back left Arsenal to join Manchester United in 1987?

10 In 1990/91 Manchester United achieved a feat no other side managed that season. What was it?

11 In their Championship year of 1997/98, Arsenal won an important match at Old Trafford by a single goal. Who notched up that winner?

12 He made a single substitute appearance for Arsenal and joined three other clubs before playing for Manchester United and England. Who was he?

13 What was the first season after the war that Arsenal met United in the FA Cup?

14 Who was the Scottish international defender who played for Arsenal in a League Cup final before joining United in the late 1960s?

15 Prior to 2000/01 who was the last Arsenal player to score three goals against Manchester United in a League match?

Answers on page 167

? ARSENAL V LIVERPOOL

1 How many times have Arsenal played Liverpool in a Second Division match?

2 In which season did Arsenal first clash with Liverpool in the FA Cup?

3 Arsenal suffered a big defeat in that first Cup meeting. What was the final score?

4 Arsenal and Liverpool competed in the first recorded game on *Match of the Day*. In what season was that?

5 Which two players were sent off for fighting in the 1963/64 FA Cup-tie at Highbury?

6 Since Liverpool's promotion back to the First Division in 1962 no Arsenal player has scored a hat-trick against them. True or false?

7 Prior to 2001/02 how many times have Arsenal played Liverpool in the FA Cup final?

8 In which years were the matches played?

9 Who were the Arsenal skippers in those three finals?

10 Who were the three Liverpool captains?

11 Prior to 2001/02 when was the last time Arsenal played Liverpool in the League Cup?

12 In that match Arsenal scored two penalty goals. Who took them?

13 Prior to 2001/02 when was the last season that Liverpool beat Arsenal both home and away?

14 Arsenal once played a League match at Liverpool's Anfield Road, but the game wasn't against Liverpool. Who were the opposition and what was the season?

15 Why did they have to play that match at Liverpool?

Answers on page 172

CLUB HISTORY – GENERAL – PART 1

Name the year of these important events in the history of Arsenal Football Club.

1 (Royal Arsenal) The club was formed.

2 (Royal Arsenal) The club entered the FA Cup for the first time.

3 (Woolwich Arsenal) The club played its first Football League Division Two game.

4 (Woolwich Arsenal) They suffered their worst-ever away defeat.

5 (Woolwich Arsenal) The club won its biggest League victory.

6 (Woolwich Arsenal) Arsenal were promoted to the First Division.

7 (Woolwich Arsenal) Arsenal finished bottom of the First Division.

8 Arsenal played their first match at Highbury.

9 Herbert Chapman was appointed manager of Arsenal.

10 Arsenal reached their first FA Cup final.

11 Arsenal won the FA Cup for the first time.

12 The West Stand was officially opened.

13 Arsenal suffered their most embarrassing defeat losing to Third Division Walsall in the FA Cup.

14 White sleeves were added to their traditional red shirts.

15 Manager Herbert Chapman died.

Answers on page 177

CLUB HISTORY – GENERAL – PART 2

Name the year of these important events in the history of Arsenal Football Club.

1 Arsenal won their fifth League title.

2 Arsenal played a prestigious friendly against Moscow Dynamo.

3 Arsenal won their first post-war Championship.

4 Floodlights were installed at Highbury.

5 The North Bank, which was destroyed during the war, was replaced.

6 The 'Busby Babes' played their final match in England.

7 The under-pitch heating system was installed at Highbury.

8 Arsenal reached their first League Cup final.

9 Bertie Mee left Arsenal.

10 Arsenal reached their third consecutive FA Cup final.

11 George Graham was appointed as Arsenal's new manager.

12 A new cantilever roof and executive boxes were installed at the Clock End of Highbury.

13 The new North Bank stand was opened.

14 Ian Wright scored three times and topped Cliff Bastin's League and Cup record.

15 Sol Campbell joined Arsenal.

Answers on page 182

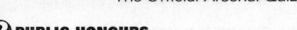

❓ PUBLIC HONOURS

Over the years many Arsenal players and personnel have received honours for military or civil achievements. Name the awards the following received.

Abbreviations:

BEM – BRITISH EMPIRE MEDAL

MM – MILITARY MEDAL

DCM – DISTINGUISHED CONDUCT MEDAL

CBE – COMMANDER OF THE ORDER OF THE BRITISH EMPIRE

OBE – OFFICER OF THE ORDER OF THE BRITISH EMPIRE

MBE – MEMBER OF THE ORDER OF THE BRITISH EMPIRE

1 Alan Ball

2 Charlie Buchan

3 Denis Compton

4 George Eastham

5 Alf Fields

6 Ken Friar

7 Arfon Griffiths

8 John Hollins

9 Pat Jennings

10 Frank McLintock

11 Bertie Mee

12 Joe Mercer

13 Billy Milne

14 Tom Whittaker

15 Billy Wright

Answers on page 186

QUESTIONS

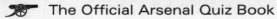

☮ THE FA CUP SEMI-FINALS – PART 3

All answers prior to season 2001/02.

1 In which season did Arsenal first reach the FA Cup semi-final?

2 What was the final score of that match?

3 Where was that semi-final played?

4 How many FA Cup semi-finals have Arsenal appeared in, including replays?

5 Of that number, how many have Arsenal won?

6 At which ground have Arsenal played most of their FA Cup semi-finals?

7 In how many seasons have semi-finals involving Arsenal gone to replays?

8 How many times have Arsenal played North London rivals Spurs in FA Cup semi-finals?

9 Who have defeated Arsenal most times in the FA Cup semi-final?

10 Arsenal once had to play four FA Cup semi-finals in the same season before they eventually won through. Name the opposition and the season.

11 And who scored the goal that saw Arsenal through to the final?

12 How many times have Arsenal won their semi-final, then lost the final?

13 Arsenal's biggest win in the FA Cup semi-final is 3–0. They have achieved this twice. Name the opposition and the seasons.

14 What is the largest attendance for an FA Cup semi-final involving Arsenal and what was the venue?

15 Including replays, how many times have Arsenal played FA Cup semi-finals in London?

Answers on page 191

❓ FAMOUS SUPPORTERS

Name these famous people who have supported Arsenal over the years.

1 The bearded character on *They Think It's All Over*

2 He fought for a title at Highbury

3 Steve Owen's widow

4 Did he really dance with wolves?

5 A disc jockey from the 1960s/70s

6 They may show him on the south of the bank

7 The Cat at Lord's

8 The lead singer of The Kinks

9 Boycie

10 A former British Grand Prix ace

11 A TV chat show host on the BBC, but it's not Parky

12 Sung for Who

13 Patrolled around Starsky

14 Lofty

15 Third in line for the throne

Answers on page 152

GREEN GUNNERS

Name the clubs from which Arsenal bought these Irishmen.

1 Terry Mancini

2 Dr Kevin O'Flanagan

3 Freddie Clarke

4 Frank O'Neill

5 Billy Dickson

6 Jack McClelland

7 Andy Kennedy

8 Jimmy Dunne

9 Pat Jennings

10 Joshua 'Paddy' Sloan

11 Eddie Magill

12 Joe Haverty

13 Noel Kelly

14 Terry Neill

15 Billy McCullough

Answers on page 157

BIRTHPLACES

The following Gunners played over 200 League games for Arsenal. Name the town where each of them was born.

1 Jimmy Bloomfield

2 Martin Keown

3 Peter Storey

4 Herbie Roberts

5 George Eastham

6 George Male

7 Brian Talbot

8 Peter 'Harry' Goring

9 Wally Barnes

10 Doug Lishman

11 Nigel Winterburn

12 Graham Rix

13 Steve Bould

14 Alex Forbes

15 Jon Sammels

Answers on page 163

❓ FA CUP FINAL DEFEATS – PART 1

All answers prior to season 2001/02.

1 How many FA Cup finals have Arsenal lost?

2 What is the scoreline they have lost by most often?

3 How many times have they lost an FA Cup final by that score?

4 Which team has beaten Arsenal the most times in an FA Cup final?

5 Arsenal lost their first FA Cup final to which side?

6 What record was set by the winners of that final, a record that still stands?

7 Arsenal lost in that final due to an unfortunate slip by their keeper. Who was he?

8 To what did Arsenal attribute that goalkeeping mistake and how did they ensure that it would never happen again?

9 In the 1932 Cup final, Arsenal's players believed that the Newcastle United equalizer should have been disallowed. What objection did they raise?

10 In the 1952 Cup final, who was Arsenal's defeated skipper?

11 Who defeated Arsenal in the 1972 Cup final?

12 Arsenal's regular goalkeeper was injured in the semi-final and missed the final. Who replaced him?

13 What was special about that final?

14 Who scored the winning goal?

15 Which Arsenal player became the first player to be booked in an FA Cup final?

Answers on page 168

❓ FA CUP FINAL DEFEATS – PART 2

All answers prior to season 2001/02.

1 In 1978 Arsenal lost a Cup final to a team a national newspaper described as 'Country Cousins'. Who were they?

2 Who was their prolific manager?

3 Who was the Gunners' boss?

4 Who scored the winning goal in that final?

5 Which two players from that winning team would later join Arsenal?

6 In which year in the 1980s did Arsenal lose a Cup final?

7 Arsenal lost that final to West Ham United who at that time were a Second Division team. True or false?

8 Who were the captains of both teams?

9 Who scored the winner with a rare header?

10 Late in that final, which Arsenal defender brought down the young West Ham midfielder Paul Allen when he was clean through on goal?

11 Which defender was the Arsenal substitute that day?

12 In 2001 what Cup final tradition was ended after 77 years?

13 What precedent did the two Cup final managers set?

14 Who scored the first FA Cup final goal at the Millennium Stadium, Cardiff?

15 It was the fourth time Arsenal had clashed with Liverpool in the FA Cup final. True or false?

Answers on page 173

CLUB CAPTAINS

All answers prior to season 2001/02.

Name the Arsenal captains who have the following distinctions:

1 He led Arsenal to their first FA Cup final victory at Wembley.

2 He skippered Arsenal to their first League Championship.

3 He led Arsenal in their first League match after the Second World War.

4 He captained Arsenal in their first European competitive match.

5 He led Arsenal in their first European Cup match.

6 He skippered Arsenal in their first European Cup Winners' Cup match.

7 He led Arsenal in their first League Cup match.

8 He lifted the League Cup for Arsenal for the first time.

9 He led Arsenal in their first Premier League match.

10 He served the longest under manager Herbert Chapman.

11 He served the longest under manager Tom Whittaker.

12 He served the longest under manager George Swindin.

13 He won the most international caps.

14 He was the first Irishman to regularly captain Arsenal.

15 He has scored the most goals for Arsenal since the war.

Answers on page 178

❓ ARSENAL IN EUROPE – THE FAIRS CUP

1 What was the full name of the first European competition Arsenal entered?

2 In which season was it first played?

3 What anniversary was celebrated by the club that season?

4 Who were Arsenal's first opponents in Europe?

5 What was the score in the first leg of that match?

6 Who scored Arsenal's first goal in that match?

7 Which two other players scored hat-tricks?

8 Which player led Arsenal into Europe as captain?

9 What was the surprising result in the return at Highbury?

10 During their first four Fairs Cup matches Arsenal used three different goalkeepers. Who were they?

11 Who were Arsenal's opponents in the second round of the competition?

12 In which country is that club based?

13 What was the aggregate score over the two legs?

14 What conditions did Arsenal encounter when they kicked off that decisive second leg?

15 Who scored Arsenal's only goal in the second leg?

Answers on page 182

ARSENAL IN EUROPE – THE EUROPEAN FAIRS CUP

1 In what season did Arsenal enter this competition?

2 How did Arsenal qualify for this competition?

3 Where was their first match played?

4 Who scored Arsenal's first goal in this competition?

5 Name the strike partnership in that first match.

6 During that season's competition Arsenal had a massive win 9–1 on aggregate. Who did they beat?

7 In the first two seasons in the competition did Arsenal lose any matches at Highbury?

8 What was Arsenal's heaviest defeat in the 1969/70 and 1970/71 series of Fairs Cup matches?

9 Who did Arsenal defeat in the Fairs Cup semi-final in 1969/70?

10 Who scored two goals over the two legs of that semi-final?

11 In 1970/71 who knocked Arsenal out of the tournament in their bid to retain the title?

12 What was the aggregate score in that match?

13 In those first two seasons in the Fairs Cup who finished top scorer for Arsenal with a total of eight goals?

14 Which player made the most appearances for Arsenal over the two seasons, and found the net six times?

15 A young goalkeeper who made only six appearances for Arsenal found a place between the posts in the first round, second leg of the Fairs Cup in 1969. Who was he?

Answers on page 187

❓ ARSENAL IN EUROPE – THE UEFA CUP – PART 1

All these questions apply to Arsenal's UEFA Cup matches in 1978/79, 1981/82 and 1982/83.

1 Arsenal's first match in this competition was against which Eastern European opposition?

2 What was the aggregate score?

3 Who scored Arsenal's first UEFA Cup goal?

4 A young wing-forward who had played only 13 matches for Arsenal came on as a substitute in that first match. Who was he?

5 In the match against Hajduk Split, Arsenal scraped through on the away-goal ruling. Which defender scored the decisive goal?

6 Who was the young 'Aussie' who made his three European appearances in the 1978/79 UEFA matches?

7 Which club knocked Arsenal out of the 1978/79 UEFA Cup?

8 What was the score?

9 Which expensive striker's only appearance was as a substitute in the last UEFA match of the 1978/79 group of games?

10 Who kept goal for Arsenal throughout the first two seasons of those UEFA matches?

11 Arsenal's 1982/83 UEFA Cup run lasted only two games. Who knocked them out of the tournament?

12 What was the embarrassing aggregate score in that match?

13 The result at Highbury was Arsenal's largest home defeat in any European match. What was it?

14 Which striker made his only European appearances for Arsenal in both legs of those matches?

15 Who scored for Arsenal in both legs of that match?

Answers on page 191

ARSENAL IN EUROPE – THE EUROPEAN CUP WINNERS' CUP

All these questions apply to Arsenal's European Cup Winners' Cup matches of 1979/80, 1993/94 and 1994/95.

1 Who were Arsenal's opponents in their first match in the European Cup Winners' Cup?

2 Arsenal did not lose a single match in that first Cup Winners' Cup season of 1979/80. True or false?

3 Who scored Arsenal's first-ever goal in the competition?

4 Which defender scored three goals that season?

5 In which stadium was the 1979/80 final played?

6 What was the result of the match?

7 A top-drawer player from each team and the Arsenal skipper missed penalties in the final. Who were they?

8 In the 1993/94 Cup Winners' Cup campaign Arsenal had a ten-goal win in one of the earlier rounds. Who were their opponents?

9 Where was the 1993/94 Cup Winners' Cup final played?

10 Who scored the goal that won the Cup for Arsenal?

11 Who made his sole Cup Winners' Cup appearance for Arsenal in that 1993/94 final?

12 In the 1994/95 Cup Winners' Cup campaign who scored nine goals?

13 What was the result of the nail-biting semi-final?

14 Who beat Arsenal in the 1994/95 Cup Winners' Cup final and by what margin?

15 Which manager was in charge of the 1994/95 Arsenal Cup Winners' Cup final side?

Answers on page 152

ARSENAL IN EUROPE – THE EUROPEAN CUP/UEFA CHAMPIONS LEAGUE

All these questions apply to Arsenal's European Cup matches of 1971/72, 1991/92, 1998/99, 1999/2000 and 2000/01.

1 What is the difference in format between the European Cup and the UEFA Champions League?

2 In the 1971/72 European Cup Arsenal had a comfortable 5–0 aggregate score in round two. Who were their opponents?

3 In 1991/92, Arsenal won their first-round home match against FK Austria Memphis 6–1. Who scored four of the goals?

4 Arsenal were eliminated that season by one of the great European sides who defeated them at Highbury in the second leg. Name those winners.

5 What was the major change for all the home matches of the 1998/99 UEFA Champions League?

6 What was Arsenal's smallest 'home' crowd in the UEFA Champions League that season?

7 In the first stages of the 1998/99 group matches Arsenal were eliminated. Where did they finish in that group?

8 Arsenal were eliminated in the 1999/2000 UEFA Champions League but were able to play in the UEFA Cup in the same season. Why?

9 How far did Arsenal get in the 2000/01 UEFA Champions League?

10 In the first group matches Arsenal were beaten 3–0, their heaviest defeat at that stage. Who were the victors?

11 What was the largest crowd Arsenal played in front of that season?

12 Who was their leading scorer in the 2000/01 Champions League?

13 Thierry Henry was the only Arsenal player to appear in every match in the 2000/01 Champions League. True or false?

14 Who finally eliminated Arsenal that season?

15 What was the final score?

Answers on page 158

ARSENAL IN EUROPE – THE UEFA CUP – PART 2

All these questions apply to Arsenal's UEFA Cup matches of 1996/97, 1997/98 and 1999/2000.

1 Which side eliminated Arsenal in the first round of the 1996/97 UEFA Cup?

2 Arsenal were beaten by the same score in both legs. What was that score?

3 Which two Arsenal players scored in both legs of that first-round match?

4 The home leg of that match was played at Wembley. True or false?

5 A young defender was a substitute in the second leg. He was transferred to a West London club in March 1997. Who was he?

6 In 1997/98 it was once again an early UEFA Cup elimination for Arsenal. Who were their conquerors?

7 What was the aggregate score?

8 Who scored Arsenal's only goal?

9 Which television channel screened both matches?

10 After elimination from the Champions League Arsenal automatically qualified for the 1999/2000 UEFA Cup. They scored six goals in the third round against which team?

11 Which player scored in both legs of that UEFA Cup match?

12 In the fourth round of the competition Arsenal scored six goals against which opposition?

13 Where was the 1999/2000 UEFA Cup final played?

14 Once again Arsenal lost a major European cup final on penalties. What was the final score?

15 Who were the players unfortunate enough to miss penalties?

Answers on page 163

OPPOSITION MANAGERS/COACHES

Name the managers/coaches of the following teams. Note: as at end of 2000/01.

1 Spartak Moscow

2 Middlesbrough

3 Charlton Athletic

4 Coventry City

5 Manchester City

6 Derby County

7 SS Lazio

8 West Ham United

9 Blackburn Rovers

10 Tottenham Hotspur

11 Southampton

12 Bayern Munich

13 Bradford City

14 Leicester City

15 Ipswich Town

Answers on page 168

GREAT SCOTS

From which clubs did Arsenal sign the following Scottish players?

1 Charlie Nicholas

2 Alex Cropley

3 Archie Macaulay

4 Sandy McFarlane

5 Johnny MacLeod

6 George Johnston

7 Jimmy Robertson

8 George Wood

9 Ian Ure

10 George Graham

11 Jackie Henderson

12 Tommy Docherty

13 David Herd

14 Bill Harper

15 Alex Forbes

Answers on page 173

ANSWERS

Ⓐ EARLY DAYS

1 The Prince of Wales public house in Plumstead.

2 1886.

3 Dial Square FC.

4 It was named after the workshop in Woolwich where the founders were employed.

5 Eastern Wanderers.

6 Dial Square won 6–0.

7 Royal Arsenal.

8 The Sportsman Ground, Plumstead Marshes.

9 The London Senior Cup.

10 Lyndhurst.

11 Arsenal won 11–0.

12 The London Charity Cup, the Kent Senior Cup and the Kent Junior Cup.

13 The Manor Ground.

14 The Invicta Ground in Plumstead.

15 Derby County.

Ⓐ IT'S ALL ABOUT CRICKET, OLD CHAP!

1 Steve Gatting.

2 Harold Hardinge.

3 Denis Compton.

4 Jim Standen.

5 Joe Hulme.

6 Jack Young (August 1952).

7 Arthur Milton.

8 Ted Drake.

9 Ray Swallow.

10 Brian Close.

11 Denis Hill-Wood.

12 Leslie Compton.

13 Don Bennett.

14 Don Roper.

15 Andy Ducat.

Ⓐ ENGLISH HEROES

1 Kenny Sansom (77 caps).

2 James Ashcroft (in 1906).

3 Arthur Milton.

4 Eddie Hapgood.

5 George Eastham.

6 Brian Talbot.

7 Wilf Copping.

8 Seven.

9 Moss, Male, Hapgood, Copping, Bowden, Drake and Bastin.

10 Danny Clapton.

11 Tony Adams.

12 Malcolm Macdonald.

13 Eddie Hapgood and George Male.

14 Spain.

15 Jimmy Rimmer.

ANSWERS

The Official Arsenal Quiz Book

FA CUP FINAL 1971 – ARSENAL V LIVERPOOL

1. The Cup and League Double.
2. Arsenal 0, Liverpool 0.
3. Bill Shankly.
4. Frank McLintock and Tommy Smith.
5. False, they changed to yellow shirts.
6. Steve Heighway.
7. George Graham.
8. The first substitute to score in an FA Cup final.
9. Don Howe.
10. John Radford.
11. Ray Clemence.
12. Norman Burtenshaw.
13. Ray Kennedy.
14. No one. At that time teams were allowed only one substitute each.
15. Five.

ARSENAL GREATS – THE COMPTON BROTHERS

1. Leslie.
2. Denis, outside-left; Leslie, centre-half.
3. Leslie.
4. Herbert Chapman.
5. Middlesex.
6. Neither, they each scored one FA Cup goal.
7. He scored ten goals in the match.
8. Division One Championship (1947/48) and FA Cup winner's medal (1950).
9. Leslie was 38 when he first played for England.

10. The oldest England debutant.
11. He scored an own goal for his country and the match was played on his home ground of Highbury.
12. May 1950 (the week after the FA Cup final).
13. 19 years.
14. CBE.
15. True.

ARSENAL GREATS – JOHN RADFORD

1. Yorkshire.
2. False, Arsenal were runners-up in 1964/65.
3. 1964.
4. False. In 1970/71 he scored 21 goals.
5. The 1968 League Cup final.
6. 41 games.
7. Arsenal's Player of the Year.
8. 1969.
9. Alf Ramsey.
10. Two.
11. Three (Billy Wright, Bertie Mee and Terry Neill).
12. Hajduk Split (Yugoslavia).
13. West Ham United and Blackburn Rovers.
14. With West Ham:1976/77–77/78, with Blackburn Rovers: 1977/78–78/79.
15. Bishop's Stortford.

ANSWERS

149

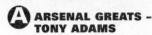

A ARSENAL GREATS – TONY ADAMS

1 1966 in Romford.

2 Sunderland.

3 Three (1989/90, 1990/91 and 1997/98).

4 66 times.

5 15 times.

6 Eight (Terry Neill, Don Howe, Steve Burtenshaw, George Graham, Stewart Houston, Pat Rice, Bruce Rioch and Arsène Wenger).

7 1988.

8 Alexander.

9 Second.

10 Yes, in 1986/87 he made the maximum 42 League appearances.

11 Against Everton on 3 May 1998.

12 Five.

13 Yes.

14 Five.

15 The 1–0 defeat by Germany at Wembley in 2000.

A THE MANAGERS – BILLY WRIGHT

1 1962.

2 CBE.

3 Wolverhampton Wanderers.

4 The first Englishman to play 100 matches for his country.

5 Joe Baker.

6 Eddie Clamp.

7 Ian Ure.

8 Liverpool in 1962/63 and 1963/64.

9 The Inter-Cities Fairs Cup.

10 Third Division Peterborough United.

11 Don Howe.

12 The team played without white sleeves on their shirts, ending a tradition from the 1930s.

13 True.

14 Joy Beverley of the singing Beverley Sisters.

15 England won the World Cup.

A CHAMPIONSHIP SEASONS – 1930/31

1 A First Division record total of points.

2 Equalled the record number of victories.

3 The least defeats in a modern first Division One season.

4 Tom Parker.

5 Jack Lambert.

6 38 goals.

7 True, Cliff Bastin.

8 Four.

9 Gerard Keyser.

10 Villa Park.

11 George Male.

12 9–1 against Grimsby Town at Highbury.

13 Chelsea.

14 Blackpool and Leicester City.

15 The London Football Combination.

CHAMPIONSHIP SEASONS – 1997/98

1 Emmanuel Petit and Marc Overmars.
2 AS Monaco and Ajax respectively.
3 Six.
4 Ian Wright.
5 12 games.
6 Derby County 3–0.
7 Matthew Upson.
8 Alex Manninger.
9 Dennis Bergkamp.
10 16 goals.
11 Paolo Vernazza.
12 Chelsea after extra time.
13 True.
14 5–0 against Barnsley and Wimbledon.
15 No one, Arsenal won the Double.

CAPITAL GUNNERS – PART 2

1 John Radford.
2 Jackie Henderson.
3 David Price.
4 Cliff Holton.
5 Andy Linighan.
6 Eddie Kelly.
7 Ronnie Rooke.
8 Malcolm Webster.
9 Peter Storey.
10 Alex Forbes.
11 Ian Wright.
12 Tommy Baldwin.
13 Bill McCullough.

14 Tommy Lawton.
15 Willie Young.

GREAT GAMES – V ANDERLECHT, 1970 FAIRS CUP FINAL

1 Ajax Amsterdam.
2 Johann Cruyff.
3 Arsenal won 4–3 on aggregate.
4 Ray Kennedy.
5 Parc Astrid.
6 RSC Anderlecht 3, Arsenal 1.
7 Ray Kennedy.
8 Bertie Mee.
9 17 years.
10 Eddie Kelly.
11 Arsenal 1, RSC Anderlecht 0.
12 Jon Sammels.
13 Tuesday.
14 51,612.
15 Jon Sammels.

(A) THE FA CHARITY SHIELD

1 1930/31.

2 Arsenal 2, Sheffield Wednesday 1.

3 Stamford Bridge, Chelsea.

4 Mainly at one of the participating clubs, normally the League Champions.

5 Arsenal 4, Manchester United 3.

6 Portsmouth and Wolverhampton Wanderers.

7 Season 1979/80.

8 Liverpool.

9 False, Arsenal have played Manchester United the most times.

10 1991/92.

11 No one, the match finished goalless.

12 Andy Cole.

13 Because Manchester United had won the Double the previous season. Arsenal were invited to play as they had finished runners-up in the Premier League.

14 Yes. In 1994 Arsenal beat Manchester United 5–4 on penalties.

15 One to One

(A) FAMOUS SUPPORTERS

1 Rory McGrath.

2 Henry Cooper.

3 Tamsin Outhwaite.

4 Kevin Costner.

5 Pete Murray.

6 Melvyn Bragg.

7 Phil Tufnell.

8 Ray Davies.

9 John Challis.

10 Damon Hill.

11 Clive Anderson.

12 Roger Daltrey.

13 David Soul.

14 Tom Watt.

15 Prince Harry.

(A) ARSENAL IN EUROPE – THE EUROPEAN CUP WINNERS' CUP

1 Fenerbahce, Turkey.

2 True.

3 Alan Sunderland.

4 Willie Young.

5 The Heysel Stadium, Brussels.

6 Arsenal lost to Valencia of Spain 5–4, on penalties.

7 Mario Kempes for Valencia, Liam Brady and Graham Rix for Arsenal.

8 Standard Liège, Belgium.

9 Copenhagen Stadium.

10 Alan Smith.

11 Steve Morrow.

12 Ian Wright.

13 Sampdoria 5, Arsenal 5. Arsenal then won 3–2 on penalties.

14 Real Zaragoza beat Arsenal 1–0.

15 Stewart Houston.

A FA CUP FINAL – 1950

1 April.
2 Arsenal 1, Liverpool 0.
3 Reg Lewis.
4 Old gold.
5 Twice.
6 Bob Paisley.
7 All seven Cup matches, including the semi-finals, were played in London.
8 He was named the Footballer of the Year by the Football Writers' Association.
9 Sixth in Division One.
10 White Hart Lane.
11 King George VI.
12 Tom Whittaker.
13 Archie Macaulay.
14 Denis Compton.
15 Arsenal skipper Joe Mercer was presented with a loser's medal before the error was spotted.

A THE NAME GAME – PART 1

1 Woody (Allen) Clive.
2 The Family (Adams) Tony.
3 Elton (John) Bob.
4 Susan (George) Charlie.
5 Tom (Jones) Bryn.
6 Sid (James) Alex.
7 Elliott (Gould) Bobby.
8 Henry (Mancini) Terry.
9 Louis (Armstrong) George.
10 Rock (Hudson) Alan.
11 Jimmy (Young) Willie.
12 Eric (Clapton) Danny.
13 Little (Caesar) Gus.

14 Ray (Charles) Mel.
15 Grace (Kelly) Eddie.

A SUPER SCOTS

1 Bob Wilson.
2 James Sharp (1906/07).
3 George Wood.
4 Charlie Nicholas (13 caps).
5 Alex James.
6 Alex Forbes.
7 Ian Ure.
8 Alex Cropley.
9 Tommy Docherty, David Herd and Jackie Henderson.
10 George Graham and Bruce Rioch.
11 Jimmy Logie or Alex Forbes.
12 Peter Marinello.
13 Bill Harper.
14 Paul Dickov.
15 Three (Archie Macaulay, Jimmy Logie and Alex Forbes).

A FA CUP FINAL 1979 – ARSENAL V MANCHESTER UNITED

1 Arsenal 2, Manchester United 0.
2 Alan Sunderland.
3 The previous season he had won a Cup winner's medal for Ipswich Town against Arsenal.
4 False, only Arsenal changed.
5 Five.
6 Terry Neill.
7 Dave Sexton.
8 Liam Brady.
9 Frank Stapleton.
10 Pat Rice for Arsenal and Martin Buchan for Manchester United.
11 Steve Gatting.
12 Four.
13 One minute.
14 Steve Walford.
15 Six (Jennings Rice, Nelson, O'Leary, Brady and Stapleton).

A ARSENAL GREATS – TED DRAKE

1 True.
2 Hampshire.
3 Southampton.
4 1934.
5 George Allison.
6 £6,500.
7 Seven.
8 42 goals (a record that still stands)
9 (c) Seven times.
10 Seven goals at Villa Park, Birmingham.
11 Five.

12 False, he scored 124 goals.
13 A flight lieutenant in the RAF.
14 The first person to play for and then manage a First Division Championship side.
15 Fulham.

A ARSENAL GREATS – PAT RICE

1 1949 in Belfast.
2 1966.
3 Burnley (as a sub).
4 1967/68.
5 1965/66. Sunderland.
6 Peter Storey.
7 The Cup and League double.
8 He was ever present throughout those seasons.
9 49 times.
10 1977.
11 Five (1971, 1972, 1978, 1979 and 1980).
12 1980. Watford.
13 He played in Arsenal's Double-winning side of 1970/71 and was assistant manager in the 1997/98 and 2001/02 Double-winning sides.
14 True, in September 1996.
15 George Best.

ANSWERS

ARSENAL GREATS – ALAN SMITH

1 Hollywood, Birmingham.
2 Leicester City.
3 1987.
4 Although Alan was signed during March, he was loaned back to the selling club for the remainder of that season.
5 A hat-trick, including his first goal.
6 16 goals.
7 The League Cup final.
8 The 1988/89 First Division Championship.
9 25 goals.
10 Saudi Arabia.
11 He played for England at amateur as well as full international level.
12 Two (Bobby Robson and Graham Taylor).
13 Five (First Division Championship twice, FA Cup, Football League Cup and European Cup Winners' Cup).
14 (c) 115 goals.
15 Nowhere, Alan was forced to retire through injury.

THE MANAGERS – BERTIE MEE

1 Physiotherapist and trainer.
2 Billy Milne.
3 Nottinghamshire.
4 March 1967.
5 Derby County and Mansfield Town.
6 Colin Addison.
7 The 1968 League Cup final.
8 Don Howe.
9 George Wright.
10 Manager of the Year.
11 OBE.
12 Seventeenth in 1975/76.
13 1976.
14 Watford.
15 General manager.

CHAMPIONSHIP SEASONS – 1932/33

1 Second.
2 True.
3 Lambert with five goals, Bastin with three.
4 118 goals.
5 Tom Parker.
6 Aston Villa.
7 True.
8 Cliff Bastin.
9 False.
10 Charlie Preedy.
11 Frank 'Tiger' Hill.
12 Walsall.
13 Tommy Black.
14 Seven (Bastin, Hapgood, Hulme, Jack, James, John and Jones).
15 Reg Stockhill.

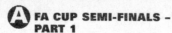

A FA CUP SEMI-FINALS – PART 1

1 Newcastle United in 1906.
2 Cliff Bastin.
3 Southampton.
4 Villa Park, Birmingham.
5 Ten.
6 1991 at Wembley.
7 Four in 1980.
8 Liverpool.
9 3–0 in 1978.
10 Chelsea, Leyton Orient and Tottenham Hotspur.
11 Seven (White Hart Lane, Tottenham four times, Stamford Bridge and Wembley (twice).
12 Christopher Wreh.
13 True.
14 Three.
15 Freddie Cox with five goals.

A THE NAME GAME – EXTRA

1 Ken (Brown) Laurie.
2 Roger (Hunt) George.
3 Alex (Young) Willie.
4 Bert (Williams) Steve.
5 Vinny (Jones) Bryn.
6 Alan (Smith) Alan.
7 John (Barnes) Walley.
8 Bobby (Robson) Stewart.
9 Tommy (Taylor) Stuart.
10 David (James) Alex.
11 Micky (Adams) Tony.
12 Sir Bobby (Charlton) Stan.

13 Ron (Henry) Thierry.
14 John (Dixon) Lee.
15 Sir Stanley (Matthews) John.

A GREAT GAMES – V SPURS, MAY 1971

1 It decided Arsenal's First Division title fate.
2 A defeat by Spurs or a scoring draw.
3 Leeds United.
4 Monday.
5 Kevin Howley.
6 Alan Mullery.
7 Peter Storey.
8 51,992.
9 Don Howe.
10 Ray Kennedy.
11 A powerful header.
12 George Armstrong.
13 (b) Joe Kinnear.
14 The referee.
15 The League Cup.

THE MISSING LINK

1 Aberdeen (Charlie Nicholas's third club).

2 Frank McLintock (all post-war captains when Arsenal won the League Championship).

3 Burnley (Ian Wright's fourth club).

4 1980 (Frank Stapleton's third Cup final appearance for Arsenal).

5 European Cup finalists (the third final Arsenal played in under Neill's management).

6 Manor Ground (Arsenal's third ground).

7 1950 (the third year that Arsenal won the FA Cup final).

8 George (Arsenal's forward line that won the 1969/70 European Fairs Cup final).

9 Doncaster Rovers (the third and final club in Jack's career).

10 Crystal Palace (Arsenal's fifth-round opponents on their route to the 1998 FA Cup final success).

11 Sunderland (Joe Baker's fifth club).

12 Coventry City (the fourth club Don Howe managed).

13 1997/98 (the second season that Arsenal completed the Double).

14 Royal Arsenal (Arsenal's second official name).

15 Olympique Marseille (Robert Pires's third club, prior to joining Arsenal).

GREEN GUNNERS

1 Queens Park Rangers.

2 Bohemians (Dublin).

3 Glenavon.

4 Home Farm (Dublin).

5 Chelsea.

6 Glenavon.

7 Crystal Palace.

8 Sheffield United.

9 Tottenham Hotspur.

10 Tranmere Rovers.

11 Portadown.

12 St Patrick's Athletic (Dublin).

13 Glentoran.

14 Bangor City.

15 Portadown.

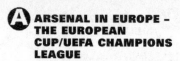

A ARSENAL IN EUROPE – THE EUROPEAN CUP/UEFA CHAMPIONS LEAGUE

1 The European Cup was played on a straight elimination basis, while the UEFA Championship has a round robin league structure with the group winners advancing to the next groups before reaching the knock-out stage.

2 Grasshopper Zurich of Switzerland.

3 Alan Smith.

4 Benfica of Portugal.

5 All matches were played at Wembley Stadium.

6 73,455.

7 Third in group E.

8 The UEFA ruling stated that any team that finished third in the Champions League was automatically accepted into the third round of the UEFA Cup.

9 To the quarter-finals of the competition.

10 Shakhtar Donetsk.

11 70,000 at Spartak Moscow.

12 Thierry Henry.

13 True.

14 Valencia.

15 The final score after the second leg was 2–2 but Valencia qualified on the away-goal ruling.

A FLOODLIT FOOTBALL

1 Arsenal's lights ran along the length of each stand, whereas other clubs' were situated on corner pylons.

2 1932.

3 The Boxers and the Jockeys.

4 Hapoel Tel Aviv, 1951.

5 Cliff Holton.

6 England v Luxembourg, World Cup qualifier.

7 England and Young England.

8 1956 (21 August), against Burnley.

9 2.15 p.m. or 2.30 p.m.

10 Both teams had to agree to play.

11 62,012 with over 10,000 fans locked out.

12 Dynamo Moscow.

13 The 1993 final against Sheffield Wednesday.

14 His Royal Highness, The Duke of Edinburgh.

15 The 1981 semi-final between Tottenham Hotspur and Wolverhampton Wanderers.

A THE NAME GAME – PART 2

1 Jimmy (Carter) Jimmy.
2 Sammy (Davis) Paul.
3 Mike (Baldwin) Tommy.
4 Harold (Wilson) Bob.
5 Robbie (Williams) Steve.
6 Lord Horatio (Nelson) Sammy.
7 Edward (Woodward) John.
8 Cyril (Smith) Alan.
9 Elizabeth (Taylor) Stuart.
10 George (Dixon) Lee.
11 Julia (Roberts) John.
12 John F. (Kennedy) Ray.
13 Brian (Rix) Graham.
14 Billy (Graham) George.
15 (Ferry) Gordon.

A WELSH WONDERS

1 Bryn Jones.
2 Caesar Augustus Llewelyn Jenkyns.
3 Derek Tapscott.
4 John Hartson.
5 Ray Daniel.
6 Wally Barnes, Dave Bowen, Derek Tapscott and Jack Kelsey.
7 John Roberts.
8 Mel Charles.
9 Dan Lewis.
10 Bob John.
11 Jack Kelsey.
12 Charlie Jones.
13 Arfon Griffiths.
14 Peter Nicholas.
15 Dave Bowen.

A ARSENAL GREATS – CHARLIE BUCHAN

1 Plumstead.
2 Arsenal and Northfleet.
3 Leyton.
4 Sunderland.
5 His 212 goals are still an aggregate record.
6 1925.
7 34 years old.
8 A transfer payment plus a bonus for every goal Charlie scored.
9 £2,700 for the 27 goals he scored.
10 False.
11 It was the first time that a non-English club (Cardiff City) had won.
12 56 goals.
13 A Lifetime in Football.
14 *News Chronicle*.
15 *Charles Buchan Football Monthly*.

ANSWERS

The Official Arsenal Quiz Book

🅐 ARSENAL GREATS – JIMMY LOGIE

1 Edinburgh.

2 1939.

3 True.

4 The Navy.

5 1946/47.

6 Wolverhampton Wanderers 6, Arsenal 1.

7 Inside-left (number 10) and left-half (number 6).

8 Nine.

9 Three.

10 League Championship 1947/48, 1952/53 and FA Cup winner 1950.

11 True.

12 It was the goal that won that season's League Championship.

13 Spartak Moscow.

14 Gravesend and Northfleet.

15 A newspaper vendor.

🅐 ARSENAL GREATS – CHARLIE GEORGE

1 The winning goal in the 1971 FA Cup final that achieved the Double.

2 Six.

3 The European Fairs Cup of 1970.

4 Blackpool.

5 He sustained a broken ankle at Everton in the first match of the season.

6 Number 11.

7 Two (1971 and 1972).

8 The 'Darling of the North Bank'.

9 1975.

10 Tottenham Hotspur.

11 Derby County.

12 24 years old.

13 False.

14 Don Revie.

15 Southampton and Bournemouth.

🅐 ARSENAL GREATS – LEE DIXON

1 Stoke City.

2 Mick Mills.

3 Steve Bould.

4 Burnley.

5 George Graham.

6 False. He signed a six-figure deal.

7 The 1988/89 First Division Championship.

8 Michael.

9 Real Madrid.

10 Ian Wright.

11 The 1984 FA Cup semi-final.

12 22 times.

13 One.

14 Bobby Robson.

15 It was his fiftieth consecutive FA Cup-tie for Arsenal.

ANSWERS

off

off

🅐🅐🅐🅐🅐🅐🅐🅐🅐🅐

THE MANAGERS –
TERRY NEILL

1 Bangor City.
2 44 caps.
3 Hull City.
4 Tommy Docherty.
5 Tottenham Hotspur.
6 Malcolm Macdonald.
7 Pat Jennings and Willie Young.
8 Four (FA Cup finals in 1978, 1979 and 1980, and European Cup Winners' Cup in 1980).
9 Liam Brady and Frank Stapleton.
10 Third in 1980/81.
11 Clive Allen.
12 Walsall.
13 Tony Woodcock.
14 Charlie Nicholas.
15 Chairman of the Professional Footballers Association.

CHAMPIONSHIP
SEASONS – 1933/34

1 Herbert Chapman and Joe Shaw.
2 George Male.
3 True.
4 Everton 3–0.
5 Ted Drake.
6 Edward 'Ray' Bowden and Cliff Bastin.
7 69,070.
8 Frank Moss.
9 Jimmy Dunne.
10 George Male.
11 Crystal Palace 7–0.
12 Aston Villa.

13 Alf Haynes.
14 True.
15 Cliff Bastin, Eddie Hapgood and Frank Moss.

FA CUP SEMI-FINALS –
PART 2

1 Leslie Compton.
2 John Radford.
3 Grimsby Town.
4 Hull City.
5 Arsenal v Tottenham Hotspur in 1991.
6 Tony Adams in 1993.
7 Ipswich Town and West Bromwich Albion.
8 George Wood.
9 Stoke City.
10 Seasons 1970/71 and 1971/72.
11 Manchester United in 1982/83.
12 Gary Lineker of Tottenham Hotspur with two goals.
13 Dennis Bergkamp in 1999.
14 Sunderland.
15 1973.

NATIVE COUNTRIES – PART 1

1 England.
2 Australia.
3 Iceland.
4 Sweden.
5 France.
6 Netherlands.
7 France.
8 Argentina.
9 South Africa.
10 Netherlands.
11 England.
12 Iceland.
13 Nigeria.
14 Denmark.
15 Grenada.

ARSENAL NOW

1 (c) N5 1BU.
2 £2.50.
3 The Gunners Shop.
4 Sir Robert Bellinger, CBE, D.Sc.
5 Gunnersaurus.
6 The flowers in the club's boardroom match the visiting club's colours.
7 Finsbury Park Station.
8 Peter Hill-Wood.
9 Commissionaires.
10 The Arsenal Museum.
11 David Dein.
12 38,500 (all seats).
13 The Chapman Lounge.
14 Vic Akers.
15 The Arsenal club crest.

TRUE OR FALSE? – PART 2

1 True.
2 True.
3 False.
4 False.
5 True.
6 False.
7 True, Charlie Buchan.
8 False.
9 True, but it wasn't the famous drag artist.
10 True.
11 False
12 False.
13 True.
14 False.
15 True.

ANSWERS

BIRTHPLACES

1. London.
2. Oxford.
3. Farnham.
4. Oswestry.
5. Blackpool.
6. London.
7. Ipswich.
8. Bishop Cleeve.
9. Brecon.
10. Birmingham.
11. Nuneaton.
12. Askern.
13. Stoke-on-Trent.
14. Dundee.
15. Ipswich.

ARSENAL IN EUROPE – THE UEFA CUP – PART 2

1. Borussia Mönchengladbach.
2. Arsenal 2, Borussia Mönchengladbach 3.
3. Paul Merson and Ian Wright.
4. False, it was played at Highbury.
5. Matthew Rose.
6. PAOK Salonika (Greece).
7. Arsenal 1, PAOK Salonika 2.
8. Dennis Bergkamp.
9. Channel 5.
10. FC Nantes Atlantique, France.
11. Marc Overmars.
12. Deportivo La Coruña.
13. Parken Stadium, Copenhagen.
14. Arsenal lost to Galatasaray of Turkey 4–1 on penalties.
15. Davor Suker and Patrick Vieira.

AUTHOR! AUTHOR! – PART 1

1. David Seaman.
2. Paul Merson.
3. Brian Marwood.
4. Ray Kennedy.
5. Wally Barnes.
6. Ian Wright.
7. Charlie Nicholas.
8. David Platt.
9. Terry Neill.
10. Bernard Joy.
11. Bob Wilson.
12. Eddie Hapgood.
13. Charlie Buchan.
14. Bob Wall.
15. Tom Whittaker.

The Official Arsenal Quiz Book

A TRUE OR FALSE – PART 1

1 False, it was Watford.
2 True.
3 False, Pat played 49 times for Northern Ireland to Sammy Nelson's 48 times.
4 True.
5 False.
6 True.
7 False, it was 'Uncle Ben'.
8 False, they are cousins.
9 False, he wore the number 11 shirt.
10 True, he was keeper for Birmingham City when they were beaten 1–0 at home by Altrincham in the FA Cup third round in 1985/86.
11 False, the record is held by Jermaine Pennant, who was 16 years and 319 days old when he played for Arsenal against Middlesbrough in the League Cup on 30 November 1999.
12 True, the other two were Tom Whittaker and Billy Wright.
13 False, it was Peter Marinello.
14 False, it was Michael Owen.
15 True.

A IRISH ICONS

1 Bill Dickson.
2 Terry Mancini.
3 Everton.
4 Dr Kevin O'Flanagan.
5 Jack McClelland.
6 Pat Rice.
7 John Devine.

8 Joe Haverty.
9 Norman Uprichard.
10 David O'Leary.
11 Niall Quinn.
12 Frank Stapleton.
13 Joshua Walter 'Paddy' Sloan.
14 Liam Brady.
15 Sammy Nelson.

A ARSENAL GREATS – BOB JOHN

1 Robert Frederick John.
2 Welsh.
3 1922.
4 Leslie Knighton.
5 Cardiff City.
6 His first cap for Wales.
7 Alf 'Doughy' Baker.
8 Four. (Division One Championship 1930/31, 1932/33, 1933/34 and FA Cup Winner 1930.)
9 Left-half (his recognised position), left-back and outside-left.
10 15 caps.
11 15 years.
12 15 years.
13 Fifth.
14 1937.
15 West Ham United.

ANSWERS

ARSENAL GREATS – JOE MERCER

1 Ellesmere Port.
2 Everton.
3 1946.
4 32 years old.
5 At Everton he was an attacking midfield general, whereas at Arsenal he was purely a defensive player.
6 George Allison.
7 False.
8 Three (Division One Championships 1947/48, 1952/53; FA Cup winners 1950).
9 Footballer of the Year.
10 Joe Wade.
11 Sheffield United.
12 OBE.
13 Malcolm Allison.
14 True (July–August 1977).
15 1990.

 ARSENAL GREATS – LIAM BRADY

1 Dublin.
2 William.
3 1971.
4 False, he was signed by Bertie Mee.
5 Millwall and Queens Park Rangers respectively.
6 1973.
7 17 years old.
8 Jeff Blockley.
9 England's manager Don Revie.
10 An FA Cup winner's medal in 1979.

11 Arsenal Player of the Year (1976, 1978 and 1979).
12 Juventus, Sampdoria, Inter Milan and Ascoli.
13 West Ham United.
14 Celtic and Brighton and Hove Albion.
15 True.

 ARSENAL GREATS – DENNIS BERGKAMP

1 Amsterdam.
2 1995/96.
3 Bruce Rioch.
4 Inter Milan.
5 He has a fear of flying.
6 David Platt.
7 79 times.
8 Denis Law.
9 True.
10 The most goals for Holland.
11 Three (a European Cup Winners' medal with Ajax and two UEFA Cup winner's medals, one with Ajax and the other with Internazionale).
12 The Football Writers' Footballer of the Year.
13 The Players' Player of the Year.
14 One (Premier League Championship 1997/98).
15 An injury kept him out of the final.

THE MANAGERS – DON HOWE

1 Caretaker manager.
2 April 1984.
3 False, he never played for Wolves.
4 1964.
5 Billy Wright.
6 (b) 70 League matches.
7 A broken leg.
8 Fairs Cup and the Cup and League Double.
9 West Bromwich Albion.
10 Four (three FA Cup finals and a Cup Winners' Cup final).
11 Paul Mariner, Viv Anderson and Steve Williams.
12 Seventh in 1984/85.
13 Steve Burkenshaw.
14 Ron Greenwood, Bobby Robson, Graham Taylor, Glenn Hoddle and Kevin Keegan.
15 Head youth coach and under-19s coach.

CHAMPIONSHIP SEASONS – 1934/35

1 George Allison.
2 Jack Lambert, David Jack, Charlie Jones and Tim Coleman.
3 Jack Crayston and Wilf Copping.
4 73,295 against Sunderland.
5 Huddersfield Town.
6 5–1 at Highbury, 6–0 at White Hart Lane.
7 Sheffield Wednesday.
8 True.
9 Reginald Trim.
10 After being injured he scored a goal as an outfield player at Everton.
11 Ted Drake.
12 42 times.
13 True.
14 Tottenham Hotspur.
15 A magnificent silver shield.

DEBUTS – PART 1

1 1994/95.
2 1931/32.
3 1983/84.
4 1955/56.
5 1996/97.
6 1954/55.
7 2000/01.
8 1980/81.
9 1997/98.
10 1969/70.
11 1991/92.
12 1936/37.
13 1983/84.
14 1974/75.
15 1977/78.

NATIVE COUNTRIES – PART 2

1. Ukraine.
2. India.
3. Libya.
4. Austria.
5. Croatia.
6. England.
7. Norway.
8. Argentina.
9. Liberia.
10. England.
11. Yugoslavia.
12. Brazil.
13. England.
14. Sweden.
15. Germany.

LEAGUE APPEARANCES

1. Liverpool.
2. Tottenham Hotspur.
3. Crystal Palace.
4. Hull City.
5. West Bromwich Albion.
6. Plymouth Argyle.
7. Hereford United.
8. Nottingham Forest.
9. Hull City.
10. Wrexham.
11. Everton.
12. Portsmouth.
13. Watford.
14. Leicester City.
15. Notts County.

ARSENAL V MANCHESTER UNITED

1. Manchester United.
2. Newton Heath (1892).
3. October 1894.
4. Dave Bowen (Arsenal) and Roger Byrne (Manchester United).
5. 1948/49.
6. David Herd and Frank Stapleton.
7. 1982/83.
8. 1968/69 (62,300).
9. Viv Anderson.
10. When they defeated Arsenal in the League Cup they became the only team to win at Highbury that season.
11. Marc Overmars.
12. Andy Cole.
13. 1950/51.
14. Ian Ure.
15. Alan Smith in 1990/91.

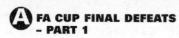

A FA CUP FINAL DEFEATS – PART 1

1 Seven.
2 1–0.
3 Five.
4 Newcastle United.
5 Cardiff City.
6 The first (and only) team outside England to win the FA Cup.
7 Dan Lewis.
8 They believed the new goalkeeping jersey was too shiny and caused the slip, so they always wash any new jersey before it is worn.
9 They claimed that the ball crossed the goal-line before the Newcastle player hooked it back into the goalmouth for his centre-forward to head it home.
10 Joe Mercer.
11 Leeds United.
12 Geoff Barnett.
13 It was the FA Cup's centenary final.
14 Allan Clarke.
15 Bob McNab.

A OPPOSITION MANAGERS/COACHES

1 Oleg Romantsev.
2 Terry Venables.
3 Alan Curbishley.
4 Gordon Strachan.
5 Joe Royle.
6 Jim Smith.
7 Sven Goran Eriksson.

8 Harry Redknapp.
9 Graeme Souness.
10 George Graham.
11 Glenn Hoddle.
12 Ottmar Hitzfeld.
13 Jim Jefferies.
14 Peter Taylor.
15 George Burley.

A AUTHOR! AUTHOR! – PART 2

1 Tony Adams.
2 George Graham.
3 Kenny Sansom.
4 Malcolm Macdonald.
5 Jack Kelsey.
6 Liam Brady.
7 Joe Mercer.
8 Alan Miller.
9 Tommy Lawton.
10 Billy Wright.
11 Frank Stapleton.
12 Alan Hudson.
13 Jon Sammels.
14 Leslie Knighton.
15 Alec Stock.

HIGHBURY STADIUM

1 Avenell.
2 1913.
3 £20,000.
4 Archibald Leitch.
5 They were not allowed to play matches on Good Friday or Christmas Day.
6 Leicester Fosse.
7 Gillespie Road.
8 73,295.
9 1935 against Sunderland (Division One).
10 A first-aid post and an ARP (air-raid precautions) Centre.
11 The North Bank Stand.
12 110yds by 73yds.
13 Ashburton Grove,.
14 60,000.
15 The East Stand is a listed Grade 2 stand, while the West Stand is also listed.

WHO AM I? – PRE-WAR

1 Cliff Bastin.
2 George Hunt.
3 Charlie Buchan.
4 Jimmy Dunne.
5 Wilf Copping.
6 Dan Lewis.
7 Andy Ducat.
8 Alf Baker.
9 Ray Bowden.
10 Eddie Hapgood.
11 Frank 'Tiger' Hill.
12 Alex James.
13 Herbie Roberts.
14 Ted Drake.
15 Joe Shaw.

ARSENAL GREATS – TOM PARKER

1 Southampton.
2 1926.
3 £3,250.
4 Herbert Chapman.
5 He made him club captain.
6 (c) 155.
7 False, he won his only international cap while a player at Southampton.
8 From the penalty spot.
9 The 1927 final against Cardiff City.
10 It was Arsenal's first major final.
11 Division One Championship in 1930/31 and the FA Cup in 1930.
12 Twice (in 1927 and 1932).
13 Six.
14 Norwich City.
15 1987.

A ARSENAL GREATS – JACK KELSEY

1 Alfred.

2 Winch Wen.

3 A blacksmith.

4 24 February 1951 against Charlton Athletic.

5 Arsenal lost at home 2–5.

6 George Swindin.

7 False, Jack's tally of 327 League appearances was passed by David Seaman.

8 True.

9 He played in goal for Great Britain against the Rest of Europe in Belfast in 1955 and for the Football League against the Scottish League at Highbury in 1960.

10 On Wednesday 26 November 1958 he played for Wales against England in the afternoon then for Arsenal against Juventus in a floodlit friendly in the evening.

11 True.

12 One (Division One Championship 1952/53).

13 November 1962.

14 Rangers.

15 He ran the Gunners Shop.

A ARSENAL GREATS – DAVID O'LEARY

1 True (Stoke Newington).

2 Manchester United.

3 Bertie Mee.

4 The FA Cup in 1979.

5 Pierce.

6 He was the first player to play in 1,000 competitive matches for Arsenal.

7 17 years.

8 Leslie Compton.

9 678 appearances and 41 times he was substitute.

10 14 times.

11 68 times.

12 One

13 Manchester United.

14 The FA Cup final replay against Sheffield Wednesday at Wembley in 1993.

15 Leeds United.

A ARSENAL GREATS – THIERRY HENRY

1 True.

2 Juventus.

3 AS Monaco.

4 The Academy of Clairefontaine.

5 Leicester City.

6 1999/2000.

7 Number 14.

8 False.

9 He held the record (with Alan Shearer) of scoring in seven consecutive Premier League matches.

10 Manchester United.

11 17 goals.

12 28 times.

13 Ten.

14 He started in every Champions League match.

15 False, it's just a habit.

The Official Arsenal Quiz Book

THE MANAGERS – GEORGE GRAHAM

1 Aston Villa.
2 Portsmouth (all clubs that George Graham played for).
3 Stroller.
4 Crystal Palace and Queens Park Rangers.
5 Terry Venables.
6 Perry Groves.
7 Theo Foley.
8 Alan Smith and Nigel Winterburn.
9 The Littlewoods Cup in 1987.
10 Only one League defeat all season.
11 Glenn Helder.
12 Six (two Championships, one FA Cup, two League Cups and one European Cup Winners' Cup).
13 Tenth in the Premier League of 1992/93.
14 1995.
15 Leeds United.

CHAMPIONSHIP SEASONS – 1937/38

1 George Allison.
2 Middlesbrough and Brentford.
3 Frank Boulton.
4 Stamford Bridge against Chelsea.
5 Herbie Roberts.
6 Ted Drake.
7 17 goals.
8 Wolverhampton Wanderers.
9 Preston North End (in the fifth round).
10 True.

11 Manchester City.
12 Reg Lewis.
13 5–0 against both Wolverhampton Wanderers and Bolton Wanderers.
14 Joe Hulme.
15 Preston North End.

DEBUTS – PART 2

1 1946/47.
2 1966/67.
3 1968/69.
4 1999/2000.
5 1946/47.
6 1962/63.
7 1926/27.
8 1957/58.
9 1997/98.
10 1937/38.
11 1953/54.
12 1926/27.
13 1997/98.
14 1934/35.
15 1994/95.

ANSWERS

171

CLUB NICKNAMES

1 The Reds or Pool.
2 The Addicks.
3 The Sky Blues.
4 The Cumbrians or The Blues.
5 The Villans.
6 The Blues or The Citizens.
7 The Rams.
8 The Saints.
9 The Magpies.
10 The Foxes.
11 The Black Cats.
12 Rangers or The Rs.
13 The Bantams.
14 The Blues or Town (unofficially Tractor Boys).
15 Rovers.

OPPOSITION GROUNDS

1 Reebok Stadium/Burnden Park.
2 Sixfields Stadium/County Ground.
3 Cellnet Riverside Stadium/Ayresome Park.
4 Britannia Stadium/Victoria Ground.
5 Pride Park Stadium/Baseball Ground.
6 Withdean Stadium/Goldstone Ground.
7 The Friends Provident St Mary's Stadium/The Dell.
8 The Kassam Stadium/The Manor Ground.
9 Sunderland Stadium of Light/Roker Park.
10 Bescot Stadium/Fellows Park.
11 The Alfred McAlpine Stadium/Leeds Road.
12 JJB Stadium/Springfield Park.
13 Adams Park/Loakes Park.
14 Madejski Stadium/Elm Park.
15 The New Den/The Den.

 ARSENAL V LIVERPOOL

1 Four (1893/94 and 1895/96, home and away).
2 1912/13.
3 4–1.
4 1964/65.
5 Arsenal's Joe Baker and Liverpool's Ronnie Yeats.
6 True.
7 Three.
8 1950, 1971, 2001.
9 1950 – Joe Mercer, 1971 – Frank McLintock, 2001 – Tony Adams.
10 1950 – Phil Taylor, 1971 – Tommy Smith, 2001 – Sammi Hyypia.
11 1996/97.
12 Ian Wright.
13 1999/2000.
14 Manchester United in 1971/72.
15 Manchester United's ground had been closed for disciplinary reasons.

FA CUP FINAL DEFEATS – PART 2

1 Ipswich Town.
2 Bobby Robson.
3 Terry Neill.
4 Roger Osborne.
5 Brian Talbot and Paul Mariner.
6 1980.
7 True.
8 Billy Bonds for West Ham, Pat Rice led Arsenal.
9 Trevor Brooking.
10 Willie Young.
11 Sammy Nelson.
12 The FA Cup final was played away from Wembley for the first time since 1923.
13 Both managers were foreign, from France, for the first time in a final.
14 Fredrik Ljungberg.
15 False, it was only the third time.

GREAT SCOTS

1 Celtic.
2 Hibernian.
3 Brentford.
4 Airdrieonians.
5 Hibernian.
6 Cardiff City.
7 Tottenham Hotspur.
8 Everton.
9 Dundee.
10 Chelsea.
11 Wolverhampton Wanderers.
12 Preston North End.

13 Stockport County.
14 Hibernian.
15 Sheffield United.

KITS, COLOURS AND SPONSORS

1 In the Champions League when the visitors' shirts clash with Arsenal's first colours.
2 SEGA.
3 Dreamcast.
4 JVC.
5 1982/83.
6 1933/34.
7 Herbert Chapman.
8 The yellow and black away shirt that incorporated the 'A' motif.
9 1992.
10 1965/66 and 1966/67.
11 Black and white stripes, black shorts.
12 1993, 1998 and 2002.
13 White shirts and blue shirts with white sleeves.
14 Black.
15 One inch red and blue stripes.

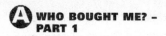

WHO BOUGHT ME? – PART 1

1 George Swindin.
2 Phil Kelso.
3 Leslie Knighton.
4 Billy Wright.
5 Don Howe.
6 Terry Neill.
7 Bruce Rioch.
8 Arsène Wenger.
9 Tom Whittaker.
10 Bertie Mee.
11 George Allison.
12 Tom Whittaker.
13 Leslie Knighton.
14 George Swindin.
15 Herbert Chapman.

WHO AM I? – 1940s/50s

1 Ted Platt.
2 Bryn Jones.
3 Stan Charlton.
4 Doug Lishman.
5 Jimmy Logie.
6 Bernard Joy.
7 Tommy Lawton.
8 Danny Clapton.
9 Wally Barnes.
10 Jimmy Bloomfield.
11 Dave Bowen.
12 Tommy Docherty.
13 Alex Forbes.
14 Harry 'Peter' Goring.
15 Vic Groves.

ARSENAL GREATS – DAVID JACK

1 The first player to score a goal in an FA Cup final at Wembley.
2 The first player to appear for different clubs in two Wembley FA Cup finals.
3 The first player to be transferred for a five-figure sum.
4 Bolton.
5 1928.
6 Charlie Buchan.
7 Four (1923, 1926 for Bolton Wanderers; 1930, 1932 for Arsenal).
8 Three (Division One Championship in 1930/31, 1932/33, 1933/34).
9 Nine.
10 True.
11 1934.
12 Southend United.
13 True.
14 113 goals.
15 The other players could not put up with his heavy smoking.

A ARSENAL GREATS – GEORGE EASTHAM

1 Ards, Northern Ireland.
2 He disputed Newcastle United's refusal to put him on the transfer list and the outcome changed the feudal retain and transfer system.
3 Jimmy Hill.
4 £47,500.
5 George Swindin.
6 Leicester City in the Football Combination (November 1960).
7 True.
8 His left.
9 Joe Baker and Geoff Strong.
10 They were the first father and son to represent England at football.
11 True.
12 19 times.
13 Alf Ramsey.
14 Stoke City.
15 The 1972 League Cup final between Stoke City and Chelsea.

A ARSENAL GREATS – KENNY SANSOM

1 The most international appearances of any Arsenal player (77 caps).
2 Leeds United.
3 Crystal Palace.
4 Malcolm Allison and Terry Venables.
5 The PFA Best Division One Left Full-Back.
6 1980.
7 True.

8 Clive Allen and Paul Barron.
9 He was bought and then sold without playing a League game for Arsenal.
10 Terry Neill.
11 Sammy Nelson.
12 True, he had won nine caps with Crystal Palace.
13 1985/86.
14 The Littlewoods Cup in 1987.
15 Newcastle United.

A THE MANAGERS – HERBERT CHAPMAN

1 Yorkshire.
2 Northampton Town.
3 Engineering.
4 Huddersfield Town.
5 1925.
6 The FA Cup in 1930.
7 Huddersfield Town 2–0.
8 They became the first southern team to win the Championship.
9 Tom Parker and Eddie Hapgood.
10 The 2–0 defeat by Walsall in the 1932/33 FA Cup.
11 Three.
12 Two League Championships (1930/31 and 1932/33) and one FA Cup success (1930).
13 1934.
14 Joe Shaw.
15 True.

THE MANAGERS – BRUCE RIOCH

1 Stewart Houston.
2 Bobby Robson.
3 Bolton Wanderers.
4 Colin Todd.
5 They appointed the first manager for 29 years to have no previous Arsenal connections.
6 Bergkamp from Inter Milan, Platt from Sampdoria.
7 Aston Villa.
8 Luton Town.
9 Alex Stock.
10 Aston Villa.
11 Tommy Docherty.
12 A League Championship medal with Derby County.
13 Millwall (all clubs Bruce had managed).
14 Scotland.
15 Fifth.

CHAMPIONSHIP SEASONS – 1947/48

1 17 matches.
2 Derby County (1–0).
3 Ronnie Rooke (with 33 goals).
4 32 goals.
5 Manchester United.
6 Maine Road.
7 18 players.
8 Ronnie Rooke and George Swindin.
9 Alf Fields.
10 Jimmy Logie.
11 Colchester United.

12 George Male.
13 Alex Forbes.
14 Wally Barnes.
15 Bradford Park Avenue 1–0.

BEFORE THE GUNNERS – PART 1

1 Coventry City.
2 Ajax Amsterdam.
3 Nottingham Forest.
4 Fulham.
5 Inter Milan.
6 Queens Park Rangers.
7 Colchester United.
8 Stoke City.
9 Juventus.
10 Torino.
11 Manchester United.
12 Brentford.
13 Everton.
14 Clapton Orient.
15 Sporting Lisbon.

Ⓐ MULTIPLE CHOICE – PART 1

1 (a) Frank McLintock.

2 (c) Ian Wright.

3 (a) Joe Baker.

4 (c) Alan Smith.

5 (b) Jack Crayston.

6 (b) Ray Kennedy.

7 (c) Bolton Wanderers.

8 (c) Paul Dickov.

9 (a) Chelsea.

10 (c) John Jensen.

11 (b) Steve Morrow.

12 (b) John Roberts.

13 c) David Rocastle.

14 b) Cardiff City.

15 (c) Tony Adams.

Ⓐ CLUB HISTORY – GENERAL – PART 1

1 1886.

2 1891.

3 1893.

4 1896.

5 1900.

6 1904.

7 1913.

8 1913.

9 1925.

10 1927.

11 1930.

12 1932.

13 1933.

14 1933.

15 1934.

Ⓐ FA YOUTH CUP

1 Six.

2 1965/66, 1970/71, 1987/88, 1993/94, 1999/2000, 2000/01.

3 1964/65.

4 (c) Seven times (1957/58, 1958/59, 1960/61, 1971/72, 1973/74, 1983/84, 1985/86).

5 1954/55.

6 Tom Whittaker.

7 Played over two legs.

8 Sunderland.

9 Pat Rice and Sammy Nelson.

10 Kevin Campbell.

11 *The Times*.

12 Manchester United.

13 Coventry City in 1999/2000, Blackburn Rovers in 2000/01.

14 Don Howe and Neil Banfield.

15 Jeremie Aliadière.

ⒶⒶⒶⒶⒶⒶⒶⒶⒶⒶ 177

(A) CLUB CAPTAINS

1 Tom Parker.
2 Tom Parker.
3 Laurie Scott.
4 George Eastham.
5 Frank McLintock.
6 Pat Rice.
7 Frank McLintock.
8 Kenny Sansom.
9 Tony Adams.
10 Tom Parker/Eddie Hapgood.
11 Joe Mercer.
12 Dennis Evans/Dave Bowen.
13 Kenny Sansom.
14 Terry Neill.
15 Cliff Holton.

(A) WHAT'S MY NAME?

1 Sulzeer (Sol) Campbell.
2 John Jensen.
3 Michael Thomas.
4 Gus Caesar.
5 David Rocastle.
6 Chris Whyte.
7 Bob Wilson.
8 Jimmy Robertson.
9 Ian Ure.
10 Tommy Docherty.
11 Jackie Henderson.
12 Con Sullivan.
13 Jimmy Logie.
14 Alex Forbes.
15 Tom Vallance.

(A) WHO BOUGHT ME? - PART 2

1 George Swindin.
2 Leslie Knighton.
3 Herbert Chapman.
4 Billy Wright.
5 Arsène Wenger.
6 Leslie Knighton.
7 George Swindin.
8 George Graham.
9 Don Howe.
10 Billy Wright.
11 George Allison.
12 Bertie Mee.
13 George Graham.
14 George Allison.
15 Tom Whittaker.

(A) WHO AM I? – 1960s/70s

1 John Radford.
2 David Court.
3 Mel Charles.
4 Pat Rice.
5 Alex Cropley.
6 Jim Furnell.
7 George Graham.
8 David Jenkins.
9 Eddie Kelly.
10 Bill McCullough.
11 Terry Neill.
12 Alan Sunderland.
13 Alan Hudson.
14 John Barnwell.
15 Brian Talbot.

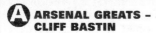

ARSENAL GREATS – CLIFF BASTIN

1 'Boy' Bastin.
2 True.
3 Exeter City.
4 £2,000.
5 1929.
6 Inside-forward.
7 The youngest-ever player to appear in an FA Cup final.
8 He was hard of hearing.
9 The club's regular penalty-taker.
10 The most goals scored by a wing-forward (33 goals in 44 matches).
11 21 caps.
12 12 goals.
13 Because of his deafness.
14 1947.
15 The most FA Cup goals scored for Arsenal (26).

ARSENAL GREATS – GEORGE ARMSTRONG

1 Hebburn, Co. Durham.
2 Geordie.
3 Electrician.
4 1961.
5 George Swindin.
6 Five feet, six inches.
7 False, he never played for England at full international level.
8 Third, behind David O'Leary and Tony Adams.
9 (a) More than 50 (he scored 68 goals).

10 The League Championship and FA Cup in 1970/71 and the European Fairs Cup in 1969/70.
11 16 seasons.
12 Barcelona.
13 Leicester City.
14 1977.
15 Reserve team coach.

ARSENAL GREATS – DAVID ROCASTLE

1 Rocky.
2 1984.
3 Newcastle United.
4 1985/86.
5 14 times.
6 1986.
7 Tottenham Hotspur.
8 True.
9 14 times.
10 No.
11 Bobby Robson.
12 1992.
13 Leeds United.
14 Hull City.
15 Tottenham Hotspur.

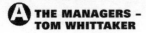

A THE MANAGERS – TOM WHITTAKER

1 Aldershot.
2 A marine engineer.
3 Centre-forward.
4 1927.
5 Secret operational work as a squadron leader in the RAF.
6 George Allison.
7 Secretary/Manager.
8 1947.
9 In his first managerial season of 1947/48 he guided Arsenal to the First Division Championship.
10 Scottish international Don Roper from Southampton.
11 Italian club Torino.
12 The League Championship in 1952/53 and FA Cup in 1950.
13 Vic Groves and Stan Charlton from Leyton Orient in November 1955.
14 1956.
15 They both died while in office.

A THE MANAGERS – ARSÈNE WENGER

1 Mutzig, Mulhouse, Strasbourg.
2 Grampus Eight Nagoya.
3 Glenn Hoddle.
4 Economics.
5 Four (1988 French Championship and 1991 French Cup with Monaco; Emperor's Cup and Japanese Super in 1996 with Grampus).
6 Pat Rice.
7 Theories on diet.
8 Third.
9 Boro Primorac.
10 Marc Overmars, Emmanuel Petit and Nicolas Anelka.
11 Manchester United.
12 The first overseas manager to win the Premiership and FA Cup Double.
13 He was voted Carling 'Manager of the Year'.
14 Vic Akers.
15 English, German, Spanish, Italian, Japanese and French.

A CHAMPIONSHIP SEASONS – 1970/71

1 Frank McLintock.
2 Nine.
3 Hillsborough, Sheffield.
4 Villa Park, Birmingham.
5 Ray Kennedy.
6 Monday.
7 Crystal Palace.
8 None.
9 A mere six goals.
10 George Armstrong, Bob Wilson and Frank McLintock.
11 FC Köln.
12 Peter Storey.
13 One.
14 Geoff Barnett.
15 Sammy Nelson.

BEFORE THE GUNNERS – PART 2

1 Nottingham Forest.
2 AS Monaco.
3 Manchester City.
4 Newcastle United.
5 Huddersfield Town.
6 Watford.
7 Northampton Town.
8 Corinthians, São Paulo.
9 Coventry City.
10 Huddersfield Town.
11 Liverpool.
12 Stoke City.
13 Sheffield Wednesday.
14 Middlesbrough.
15 Stockport County.

MULTIPLE CHOICE – PART 2

1 (a) Kenny Sansom.
2 (a) Eddie Hapgood.
3 (b) Andy Cole.
4 (c) Millwall.
5 (b) Theo Foley.
6 (b) David Miles.
7 (b) Willie Young.
8 (a) The Milk Cup.
9 (a) Queens Park Rangers.
10 (c) George Cox.
11 (b) AS Monaco.
12 (a) The 1980 final.
13 (b) Bertie Mee.
14 (b) One shilling.
15 (c) 1912/13.

ARSENAL AT WAR

1 The playing sequences for the film *The Arsenal Stadium Mystery*.
2 Three.
3 Arsenal 5, Sunderland 2.
4 South 'A' and South 'C'.
5 Preston North End (they lost two goals to one after a drawn match).
6 Wembley, with the replay at Ewood Park, Blackburn.
7 As a first-aid post and ARP Centre.
8 White Hart Lane, Tottenham.
9 The North Stand
10 Reg Lewis.
11 Charlton Athletic, who were defeated 7–1 with Reg Lewis scoring four times.
12 Stan Mortenson.
13 To man the air-raid post at the top of the main stand.
14 Drake, Crayston, Hapgood and Kirchen.
15 Moscow Dynamo.

A N S W E R S

A CLUB HISTORY – GENERAL – PART 2

1   1938.
2   1945.
3   1948.
4   1951.
5   1956.
6   1958.
7   1964.
8   1968.
9   1976.
10 1980.
11 1986.
12 1989.
13 1993.
14 1997.
15 2001.

A ARSENAL IN EUROPE – THE FAIRS CUP

1   The Inter-Cities Fairs Cup.
2   1963/64.
3   The 50th season at Highbury.
4   Staevnet (Copenhagen).
5   Staevnet 1, Arsenal 7.
6   Johnny MacLeod.
7   Geoff Strong and Joe Baker.
8   George Eastham.
9   Arsenal 2, Staevnet 3.
10 Iain McKechnie, Bob Wilson and Jim Furnell.
11 Royal Football Club, Liègeois.
12 Belgium.
13 Arsenal 2, Royal Football Club 4.
14 Two inches of snow.
15 Billy McCullough.

A AFTER THEY WERE GUNNERS – PART 1

1   Celta Vigo, Spain.
2   Queens Park Rangers.
3   Bristol City.
4   Southampton.
5   Manchester City.
6   Celtic.
7   SM Caen, France.
8   Watford.
9   Juventus, Italy.
10 West Ham United.
11 Queens Park Rangers.
12 Nottingham Forest.
13 Gravesend and Northfleet.
14 Newcastle United.
15 Huddersfield Town.

THE MAGNIFICENT MACS

1 Jimmy McGill.
2 Billy McCullough.
3 Eddie McGoldrick.
4 Johnny MacLeod.
5 Frank McLintock.
6 Archie Macaulay.
7 Malcolm Macdonald.
8 John 'Jack' McClelland.
9 Gavin McGowan.
10 Ian McPherson.
11 Bob McNab.
12 Ian McKechnie.
13 Alex Mackie.
14 Brian McGovern.
15 Brian McDermott.

WHO AM I? – 1980s/90s

1 Stefan Schwarz.
2 Gilles Grimandi.
3 Martin Keown.
4 Glenn Helder.
5 Steve Morrow.
6 Alan Miller.
7 Nigel Winterburn.
8 Gary Lewin.
9 John Lukic.
10 Luis Boa Morte.
11 Lee Dixon.
12 Nicolas Anelka.
13 Alan Smith.
14 Paul Merson.
15 David O'Leary.

ARSENAL GREATS – GEORGE MALE

1 He worked for Lloyd's insurance.
2 Arsenal beat Blackpool 7–1.
3 1930.
4 Tom Parker.
5 Left-half.
6 19 caps.
7 Yes.
8 Six (Division One Championship 1932/33, 1933/34, 1934/35, 1937/38, 1947/48; FA Cup winner 1936).
9 Yes (1932).
10 1948.
11 Arsenal beat Grimsby 8–0 to clinch the Championship.
12 None.
13 18 years.
14 Coach to Arsenal juniors and chief scout.
15 88 years old.

ANSWERS

ARSENAL GREATS – JOE BAKER

1 Liverpool.
2 Chelsea.
3 Hibernian.
4 Torino, Italy.
5 Denis Law.
6 He was involved in a serious car crash.
7 1962.
8 £67,500.
9 Billy Wright.
10 Geoff Strong.
11 106 goals.
12 Albion Rovers.
13 Three caps.
14 He was the first player based at a 'foreign' club to play for England.
15 He was in the 1966 World Cup pool of 40 players.

ARSENAL GREATS – IAN WRIGHT

1 1991.
2 Crystal Palace.
3 Steve Coppell.
4 True.
5 24 goals.
6 A labourer and plasterer.
7 Four (two for Crystal Palace, two for Arsenal).
8 Ted Drake.
9 Ferenc Puskas.
10 184 goals.
11 Cliff Bastin, who had held the record with 176 goals.
12 1998.

13 West Ham United
14 27 times.
15 Nine.

THE MANAGERS – JACK CRAYSTON

1 Assistant manager.
2 November 1956.
3 For the first time they did not ask the manager to combine his post with that of secretary.
4 True.
5 Derek Tapscott.
6 West Bromwich Albion.
7 John Barnwell.
8 The 'Busby Babes' of Manchester United played their last match at Highbury.
9 Jim Standen.
10 Dave Bowen.
11 Fifth in 1956/57.
12 Bob Wall.
13 The FA Cup fourth-round defeat by Northampton Town on 4 January 1958.
14 24 years.
15 Doncaster Rovers.

A MANAGING AFTER THE GUNNERS – PART 1

1 Blackpool.
2 Nottingham Forest.
3 Sheffield United.
4 Northampton Town.
5 Blackburn Rovers.
6 Hull City.
7 West Bromwich Albion.
8 Bishop's Stortford.
9 Reading.
10 West Bromwich Albion.
11 Peterborough United.
12 Stoke City.
13 Bournemouth and Boscombe.
14 Portsmouth.
15 Crystal Palace.

A BEFORE THE GUNNERS – PART 3

1 Real Mallorca.
2 Leicester City.
3 Tottenham Hotspur.
4 Cardiff City.
5 Liverpool.
6 Southampton.
7 Dynamo Kiev.
8 Benfica.
9 Wolverhampton Wanderers.
10 AC Milan.
11 Hibernian.
12 Bradford Park Avenue.
13 Everton.
14 Southampton.
15 Preston North End.

A CHAMPIONSHIP SEASONS – 1988/89

1 Tony Adams.
2 Alan Smith.
3 Steve Bould.
4 45,129.
5 Tottenham Hotspur.
6 Kevin Richardson.
7 Nigel Winterburn, John Lukic and David Rocastle.
8 Alan Smith.
9 Niall Quinn.
10 West Ham United.
11 Liverpool.
12 Villa Park.
13 Michael Thomas.
14 Bruce Grobbelaar.
15 It was practically the final kick of the final match of the season.

ANSWERS

GREAT GAMES – V NEWCASTLE, 1952 FA CUP FINAL

1 False~, they had played them in the 1932 FA Cup final.
2 Third position.
3 Ray Daniel.
4 Jimmy Logie.
5 White Hart Lane, Tottenham.
6 Chelsea.
7 Arthur Milton.
8 Alex Forbes, Jimmy Logie and Cliff Holton.
9 Wally Barnes.
10 Don Roper.
11 55 minutes.
12 Doug Lishman.
13 George Robledo.
14 The first club to win the FA Cup in consecutive seasons.
15 Skipper Joe Mercer.

FA CUP APPEARANCES

1 Liverpool.
2 Manchester United.
3 Ipswich Town.
4 Chelsea.
5 Liverpool.
6 Bolton Wanderers.
7 Manchester United.
8 Wolverhampton Wanderers.
9 Newcastle United.
10 Ipswich Town.
11 Tottenham Hotspur.
12 Chelsea.
13 Everton.
14 Aston Villa.
15 Tottenham Hotspur.

PUBLIC HONOURS

1 MBE
2 MM
3 CBE
4 OBE
5 BEM
6 OBE
7 MBE
8 MBE
9 MBE and OBE
10 MBE
11 OBE
12 OBE
13 DCM
14 MBE
15 CBE

ANSWERS